C000220778

GUIDE TO THE DEVON AND DORSET WORLD HERITAGE SITE

THE JURASSIC COAST

RODNEY LEGG

DORSET PUBLISHING COMPANY

First published in Great Britain in 2002

British Library Cataloguing-in-Publication Data
A CIP record for this title is available from the British Library

ISBN 0 948699 77 9

DORSET PUBLISHING COMPANY

National School
North Street
Wincanton
Somerset
BA9 9AT

Printed and bound in Italy by Centro Grafico Ambrosiano, Milan

In memory of Roland Gant who walked and swam its entire length

Introduction

The Jurassic Coast of Devon and Dorset has joined the Grand Canyon and the Great Barrier Reef as a World Heritage Site. It is the first natural landscape in Great Britain to win this highest of international accolades, granted by the World Heritage Committee of the United Nations Educational, Scientific, and Cultural Organization (Unesco), meeting in December 2001 in Helsinki. Across the water, its geological sister site is the volcanic Giant's Causeway in Northern Ireland, and at home the archaeological surroundings of Stonehenge and Avebury are the closest partners. Overseas the list includes the Pyramids and the Taj Mahal.

The other three British additions in 2001 reflected the national role as the cradle of the Industrial Revolution. New Lanark was created as a model industrial community by pioneer socialist Robert Owen. Saltaire village near Bradford was built by textile magnate Sir Titus Salt. Mills along the Derwent valley introduced mass production after Sir Richard Arkwright introduced water-powered silk throwing and cotton spinning.

Nomination of the Jurassic Coast reflected the call from Unesco for more natural as distinct from man-made sites. It is described as Jurassic for its famous dinosaur-bearing strata but the visual geology extends on either side of this period. It crosses the Mesozoic era from Triassic desert sands, before the Jurassic sea, followed by Cretaceous rivers and lagoons and a marine environment with the chalk.

From Orcombe Point at Exmouth to Old Harry Rocks, beside Studland Bay, this coast provides a walk in time through 180 million years in just 160 kilometres, plus fossils new to science which appear as it continues to erode. There is no other equivalent sequence on Earth which is exposed in the same way. Unique is the ultimate superlative for the jewel in the crown of textbook geology.

Richard Offen, speaking for the National Trust as its campaign manager for Enterprise Neptune, expressed 'Jurassic joy' that 'this spectacular stretch of coastline' – of which the Trust owns 64 kilometres – had been given such a prestigious layer of acclaim and protection: 'This coast already attracts large numbers of visitors during the summer months but the broader designation should ensure that interest continues through the winter months as well because of the scientific interest and the constant exposure of the coastline due to erosion. We are looking forward to working with all the other partners to ensure that the region and the nation benefits, as we offer improved visitor facilities, information and interpretation and eco-tourism opportunities.'

The National Trust, overall around England, Wales and Northern Ireland, owns 16 per cent of the coastline. Between Orcombe Point and Old Harry Rocks (both Trust owned), along the newly designated 160 kilometres, its rate of ownership rises to a remarkable 42 per cent (extending to 64 kilometres). The Landslip National Nature Reserve west of Lyme Regis is managed by English Nature and blue lias cliffs on each side of the town have been at the forefront of pioneering earth sciences for three centuries. In the eastern third, in the area of Purbeck District Council from White Nothe to St Alban's Head and onwards around Anvil Point to Ballard Down, other substantial public owners include the Ministry of Defence (the Lulworth Ranges) and Dorset County Council (Durlston Country Park).

A Unesco spokesman pointed out that the United Kingdom was a relatively recent signatory to the World Heritage Convention and said many delegates felt that future additions to the list of 622 sites should favour under-represented areas in Africa, Asia and South America. So for now the next 25 potential sites on a tentative list drawn up by the Department for Culture, Media and

Sport may have a long wait for consideration. They include Chatham Naval Dockyard and Isambard Kingdom Brunel's Great Western Railway from Paddington to Bristol.

None has the quality of our scenic coast which is listed here in gazetteer format from west to east. As a concession to metrication the distances are given in metres, but out of respect for history and in line with Civil Aviation Authority requirements, heights are in feet. Map references are given for recommended parking places and to the more obscure places of interest. Parking opportunities are limited and far from where you might wish to be, though visual access can often be almost as breathtaking as physical experience. I balk, however, at the trendy concept of 'intellectual access' as that makes it sound like a virtual reality coastline. Ours is beyond compare and one hopes that Unesco will continue with its policy of quality rather than quantity.

All visitors have to start somewhere and every year hundreds of teachers can hardly be wrong. From all over Britain they descend on Lulworth Cove and fan out into an incredible outdoor classroom along the cliffs between White Nothe in the west and Tyneham Cap in the east. A few determined characters will be inspired to walk our entire coastline.

Map Locations

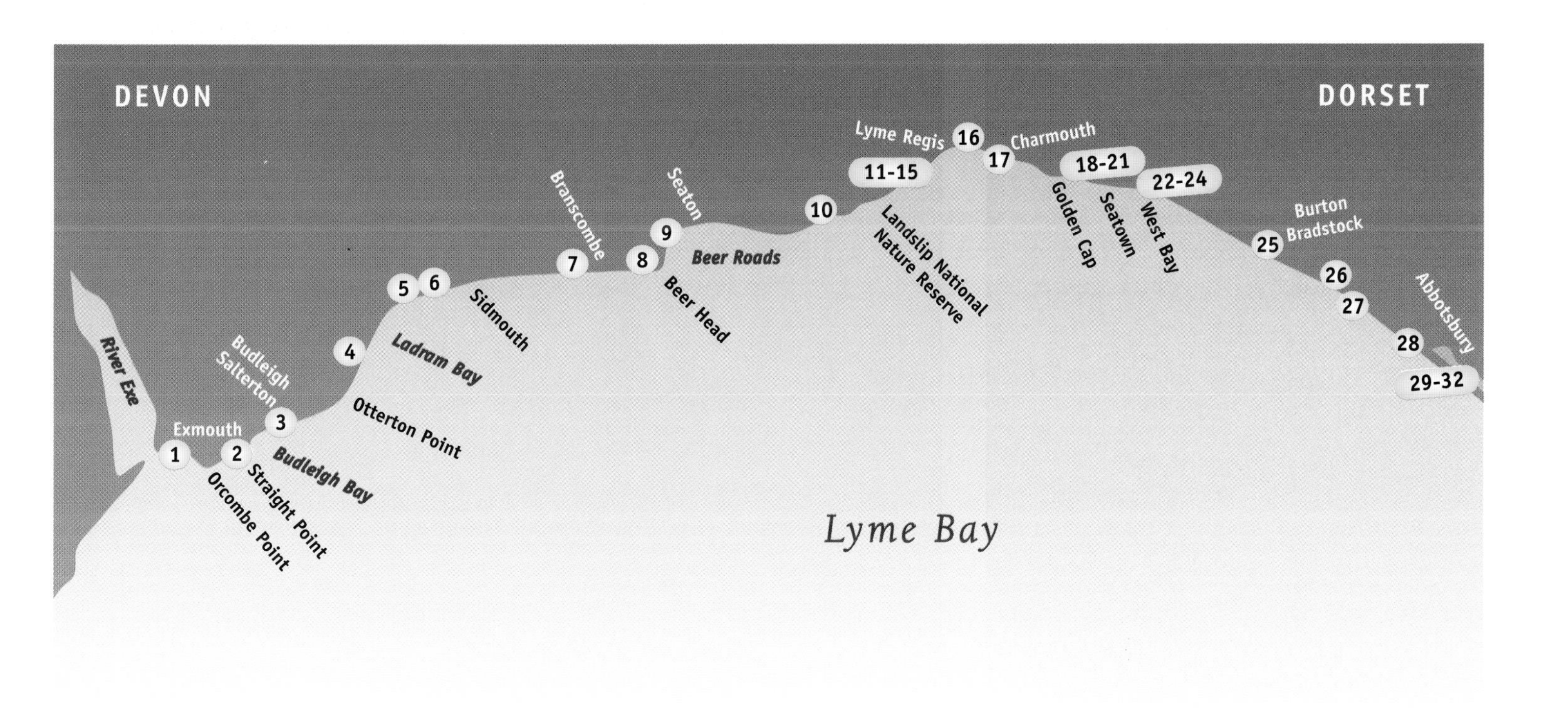

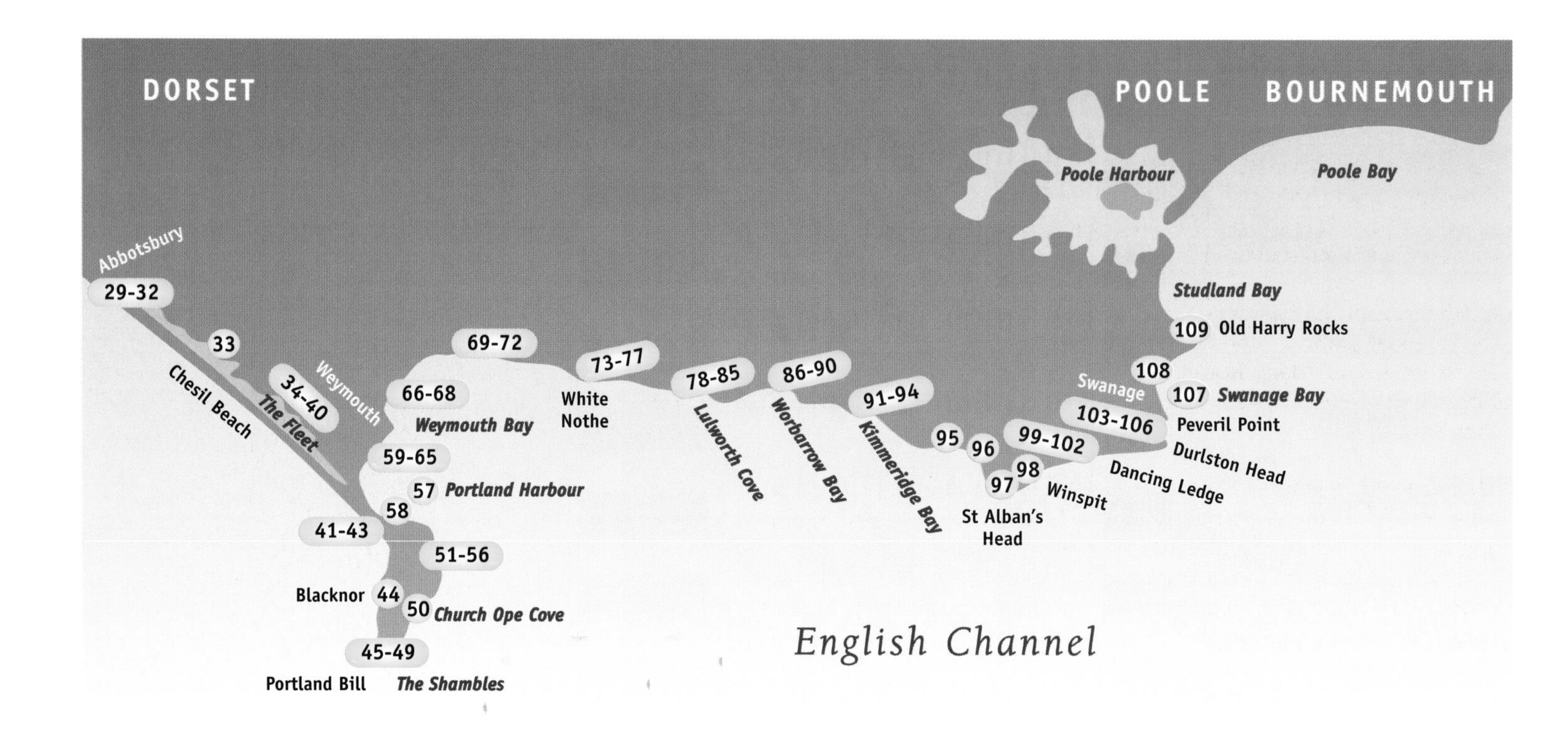
DORSET
POOLE
BOURNEMOUTH
Poole Harbour
Poole Bay
Abbotsbury
29-32
33
Chesil Beach
34-40
The Fleet
Weymouth
66-68
69-72
Weymouth Bay
73-77
White Nothe
78-85
Lulworth Cove
86-90
Worbarrow Bay
91-94
Kimmeridge Bay
59-65
57 Portland Harbour
58
41-43
51-56
Blacknor 44
50 Church Ope Cove
45-49
Portland Bill
The Shambles
English Channel
95
96
97
98
St Alban's Head
Winspit
99-102
Dancing Ledge
103-106
Swanage
108
107 Swanage Bay
Peveril Point
Durlston Head
109 Old Harry Rocks
Studland Bay

The Jurassic Coast

1 EXMOUTH and ORCOMBE POINT

Exmouth seagull: the World Heritage Site begins after the last groyne.

Red sandstone cliffs, rising to 250 feet, are reached from a car-park at The Maer towards the south-eastern extremity of Exmouth and the Exe estuary (Ordnance Survey map reference SY 004 802). The River Exe crosses Devon from Tiverton after dropping down from the hill country of West Somerset which carries its name – Exmoor. There it is fast flowing and rocky with bursts of white-water rapids. Beside Exmouth it is tired and tidal.

Offshore from the Esplanade and its Marine Drive continuation – eastwards from the Lifeboat Station – the beach ends at the Conger Rocks. Inshore the red sandstone ledges of Maer Rocks and Orcombe then sandwich a nature reserve at Rodney Point below the final crescent of houses and bungalows 1000 metres from the car-park.

The next 1200 metres of clifftop, around Orcombe Point, are owned by the National Trust and go by the descriptive name of the High Land of Orcombe with turf on top and brambles below. Landward is the ancient house of Pratshayes which with 126 acres was bequeathed to the Trust by Miss E. H. Pratt in 1960. The descent to the foreshore is by Rodney Steps or Orcombe Point Steps. Sandy Bay, below the red cliffs, is a mixture of sand and shingle.

Beyond the Trust's property, stretching inland for a kilometre to West Down Farm, is the vast Devon Cliffs Holiday Park. It is offset, seawards, by the grassy expanse of Straight Point and Otter Cove, but this doubles as a rifle range and is out of bounds. Lyme Bay curves inland in a great sweep and you are now at the same latitude as Weymouth with Portland at the extremity of the view in that direction and Start Point behind you on the Devon side.

Exeter features in the Anglo-Saxon Chronicle for the years 1001 and 1003. In the latter, according to the most detailed manuscript: 'Swein, King of the Danes, through the evil counsel, negligence, or treachery of the Norman count Hugh, whom Queen Emma had put over Devon, stormed and despoiled the city of Exeter, and destroyed the wall from the east to west gate.'

Orcombe Point: sandstone headland jutting out from the Exe estuary.

Exmouth became Exeter's port, supplying ten ships with 190 men for King Edward III's year-long siege of Calais, which was brought to a successful conclusion on 4 August 1347. For Exmouth, its revival as the local seaside spa – as the watering place for Exeter families – took place in the eighteenth century, taking advantage of the long sandy beach. In the town, Bath Road says it all, both in its name and visually in terms of Georgian aspirations and fashionability. Two famous widows lived at red-brick No. 6 Bath Road and Italianate No. 5. They were Frances, Lady Nelson, and Anne Isabella, Lady Byron. Holy Trinity church, completed in 1824 and since expanded, rises cathedral-size nearby.

Offshore at low tide, on the other side of the Exe, a multitude of waders feed on the rich silt of Pole Sand which stretches for 3 kilometres, westwards to Dawlish Warren and Langstone Point.

Littleham Cove: eastwards across The Floors to Budleigh Bay.

2 STRAIGHT POINT and LITTLEHAM COVE

East facing, and generally out of the prevailing wind, Littleham Cove is reached from Littleham village at the eastern edge of Exmouth's suburbs (SY 029 812). Continue on foot from the Clinton Arms, along West Down Lane and follow a public footpath south-eastwards beside West Down Farm and through the arch proclaiming 'Sandy Bay' into Devon Cliffs Holiday Park. The cliffs are a kilometre away. It is a land of occasional palms and what can only be described as a confusion of caravans and leisure facilities between National Trust fields and the security wire of Straight Point Rife Range.

Somewhat incongruously, amid caravans that cover 250 acres, active military assets are set in the middle of the holiday coast. Eyes and weapons on the top of the knoll look eastwards and fire that way, overshooting into Budleigh Bay, with a sea of static vans behind them and to their left.

Here we join the coastal footpath and can turn eastwards to climb above the landslipped slopes of The Floors to West Down Beacon. This is the great Devon seascape of western Lyme Bay. The path climbs stiffly to the Ordnance Survey triangulation pillar at 424 feet above Budleigh Bay and then drops almost as sharply to the golf course west of Budleigh Salterton in a kilometre. Inland, arable fields show the distinctive Devon red earth, and one pastoral farm still had North Devon red cattle when I passed. Pebbles range in colour from grey and pink through to dull browns.

3 BUDLEIGH BAY and BUDLEIGH SALTERTON

The Frinton of Devon has been credited with the highest proportion of old-age occupancy in the British Isles and is best explored from its eastern car park, at the far end of the promenade (SY 073 820). Beyond Budleigh Bay the onward course of the South West Coast Path is thwarted by the estuary of the River Otter and seaward Otterton Ledge which acts as a natural groyne to the nearby town. Salterns around the haven give the town its name.

West Down: the cliff path out of Budleigh Salterton.

Eastern beach: towards the River Otter.

Sir John Millais set up his easel on the beach and painted the 'Boyhood of Raleigh'. A plaque marks the spot beside a stone ball set on a short section of seaside wall. The picture made its sensational debut at the Royal Academy in 1870. It is a reminder that Sir Walter Ralegh (the contemporary spelling) was born at Hayes Barton, nearby, in 1552 and remains the most famous local lad.

River Otter: straight and tidal from Otterton.

The river rises in Somerset's Blackdown Hills, and comes via Honiton, leaving its name at Ottery St Mary which has the vicarage where Samuel Taylor Coleridge was born in 1772. John Leland recorded this estuary as a harbour for a hundred vessels in 1540 but silting and the onward trend in shipping tonnage has done for it since. It is still a convincing obstacle for walkers and the path detours inland and northwards to White Bridge in a kilometre before doubling back beside the Scot's pines on the east bank to South Farm and Danger Point.

There are no other public paths to link these cliffs with either Otterton Park or Otterton village. The only access is to continue along the clifftop for 3 kilometres to Coal Beach, Black Head, Poolness Beach, Brandy Head, Twopenny Loaf Rock, Crab Ledge and Chiselbury Bay.

4 LADRAM BAY and HIGH PEAK

Bell Street and other lanes east of Otterton village (SY 085 853) lead for a kilometre to a choice of paths from Monks Wall and Bay Road down to Ladram Bay Holiday Camp in a sylvan setting on the cliffs between the offshore Smallstones Point rocks and picturesque Ladram Rock. In fact there are three columns of sandstone rising from Ladram Bay, as commemorated in the modern Three Rocks Inn (SY 097 853) on the viewpoint above the cottage ornée and the hollow down to the shingle. From here the path heads northwards, across the grass beside a scrubby outcrop of cliff, into the next stunning seascape.

Below – *Ladram Rock: on the beach in Ladram Bay.*
Below right – *Coral encrusted: the reef-like base of Ladram Rock.*

There are another five towering stacks, topped with sea-birds and their guano, 200 feet above rock pools and a sequence of intermittent ledges and slabs continues for a kilometre. Otterton, for its thatch, and the red and blue views in both directions from the Three Rocks Inn is as chocolate box as anywhere in Devon and Dorset. You may well have feelings of déjà vu.

The route is north-eastwards to Hern Point Rock, Sandy Bay, Conger Pool, Little Picket Rock, Big Picket Rock, Green Point and Wheel Rock, before extending across the Lade Foot ledges to Tortoiseshell Rocks beside the sands west of Sidmouth.

Inland, pine trees and a thicket across the 514-feet summit of High Peak conceal the earthworks of a small Iron Age hill-fort, followed by the appropriately named Windgate as a saddle of pastures sloping away from the landslipped cliffs.

Nesting peaks: with great black-backed top-most and herring gulls below.

The rocks: below Three Rocks Inn.

Woolbrook Glen: now the Royal Glen Hotel.

5 PEAK HILL and WOOLBROOK GLEN

The plateau of Peak Hill and Muttersmoor Plantation extends northwards from the coast road west of Sidmouth and rims a deep bowl-shaped valley, with parking on the scrubby 548-feet summit (SY 109 873), which as with so much of this coast is owned by Clinton Devon Estates.. On the Sidmouth side of the hill, 25 acres of cliff and slopes were acquired for the National Trust in 1985 through a bequest by Miss A. Farewell Jones and the Sidmouth Landscape Appeal Fund.

In Western Town, just 150 metres inland along Glen Road (SY 122 872), stands Woolbrook Glen – now part of the Royal Glen Hotel – which was the setting for a crucial twist of fate for the British monarchy. Plaques historic and modern remind us that it was into this elegant setting that the Duke and Duchess of Kent moved, with their infant daughter Princess Victoria, on Christmas Eve in 1819.

The Duke was down on his luck both physically and financially. Devon seemed to offer a healthy respite for both but in the event it killed rather than cured. He expired within the month, on 23 January 1820, and baby Princess Victoria was heir to the throne, becoming Queen Victoria in 1837.

Millennium plaque: reminding us about time and tide.

6 TOWN BEACH at SIDMOUTH

The pebbles and gravel of Town Beach stretch for a kilometre either side of Sidmouth where the River Sid meanders through the length of the town before disappearing under the Esplanade east of Victoria Hotel and the Belmont Hotel (SY 129 872). There are just two sandstone exposures rippling seawards at Chit Rocks and Chapman's Rocks. Peak Hill Road rises to the west and the Regency-style Rock Cottage on the seafront was bequeathed to the National Trust in 1990 by Dr H. R. Vernon though it is not open to the public. Sidmouth people have long been avid supporters of the Trust and have also preserved meadows on both sides of the Sid in the middle of the town.

Chit Rocks, in Western Town, mark the site of a thirteenth-century harbour which curved seawards like The Cobb at Lyme Regis. It was swept away by a series of gales and Sidmouth slipped into obscurity until the wealthy rediscovered the seaside. 'Nov 1834' is the datestone in the sea-wall below Rock Cottage and a nearby plaque records the opening of the 1999-built Clinton Walkway, heading westwards along the bottom of the wall. It was constructed by the Sidmouth Millennium Walkway Group.

From the eastern edge of Sidmouth the South West Coast Path climbs Salcombe Hill Cliff, where Vaughan Cornish dedicated land as public open space in 1937, and then drops into a deep-cut valley at South Combe where it detours a short distance inland before crossing a stream in the gully, with National Trust land forming the next slope, these 61 acres having been bought through the local appeal in 1990. The path slips and slides in places with only a tenuous grip on the landscape as the underlying geology changes from sandstone to clay with lumps of flint-like chert.

A fine Roman bronze statuette, featuring Achilles riding Chiron the centaur with a hound reaching up to them, was found on Sidmouth beach and is now in Exeter Museum.

River Sid: trickles across shingle into the sea.

7 DUNSCOME to BRANSCOMBE

Six kilometres of cliffs from Higher Dunscombe to beyond Branscombe are in National Trust ownership with the closest car-park being beside the ford south of the Tudor farm named Great Seaside at Branscombe Mouth (SY 207 882). Here the tavern is the Sea Shanty. Up the valley, in Branscombe village, old cottages bear the sign of Ye Olde Masons Arms. The Forge, National Trust owned, is believed to be the last working thatched forge in the country. Andrew Hall is the blacksmith.

Precipitous coast: eastwards to Higher Dunscombe Cliff.

National Trust ownership covers 681 acres, including Coxes Farm and two mediaeval farmhouses at Branscombe, with the land having been acquired through a series of bequests and donations between 1965 and 1991. A public footpath also climbs through the sloping pastures and woods from the crenellated tower of St Winifred's parish church at Branscombe to link with the coastal path, in 300 metres, beside a string of disused quarries above Berry Cliff.

Westwards, in 700 metres, the rampart of Berry Camp encloses a large Iron Age settlement on the clifftop above Branscombe Ebb. Approaching the other way, via Dunscombe, involves a punishing descent at Weston Mouth, with a kilometre-long detour up and around Weston Combe if it turns into a slope too far. Red cliffs have white tops where chalk overlies the sandstone.

Great Seaside: Tudor farmstead at Branscombe.

Most of Branscombe is tucked away without a view of sea. It includes the thatched Bakery, worked by brothers Gerald and Stuart Collier until 1987, which had the last traditional faggot-fuelled ovens in Devon. Such methods then fell foul of health and safety regulations. The National Trust has preserved the baking room as a museum piece and turned the rest of the cottage into a tea-room.

Manor Mill, however, has continued to turn. Its millstones are powered by a water-driven wheel and working demonstrations of the milling process take place on

Sunday afternoons in late summer ('water levels permitting,' the National Trust reminds us).

Returning to the parish church at Branscombe, it gives me a chance to mention my predecessor and mentor, Roland Gant. He wryly noted that of its wall-paintings of the Seven Deadly Sins, 'the only one to survive is Lust, as probably it always does'. My current informant, Tony Poyntz-Wright, shows more interest in the grave of an Excise officer killed by smugglers and recalls ancient Bovey House as having provided his best ever holiday. The only disappointment for Tony and Di, having walked to Salcombe Regis in sweltering heat, was failing to find a public house or shop when they were desperate for an ice cream.

On the theme of lust and love, we read that a fertile young Elizabethan from Branscombe, Joan Tregarthin, married John Kelaway and provided him with 14 children. She then married John Wadham and produced six more. Of the twenty, from the second batch, it is Nicholas who is remembered. He provided the endowment that founded Wadham College, Oxford, in 1610.

Chalk columns: rising from sandstone footings beside beach-huts at Branscombe.

8 BEER HEAD

The red cliffs turn to white as Beer Head projects from behind Arratt's Hill, a kilometre south from Beer, where the parking is at the southern end of the little town (SY 228 887). Coming from the other direction, below South Down Common – after leaving National Trust land at Branscombe – we continue eastwards for a kilometre to Beer Head. There are two options for following the coastal path. One route is along the top of the cliff and the other midway down across the slopes of Under Hooken.

Beer Head rises sheer to 100 feet and then continues more gradually as it trebles in height. It and the curtain of white cliffs to Beer are like a piece of Sussex in Devon, as these are the most westward outliers of the English chalk, being the final Cretaceous formations before you reach America.

A big landslip occurred on Hooken Cliffs (SY 219 881) in March 1790. Between 7 and 10 acres of cliff collapsed, from between 200 and 260 feet above sea level and dropped into the sea. It came to rest beside the Sherborne Rocks. The incident happened at

Beer Roads: empty anchorage when the boats are safely beached.

night, and went unseen, but it was a clear night and Beer fishermen were alarmed by the sounds of 'convulsion'. They were even more astonished in the morning to find crab-pots that had been laid offshore at depth of eight feet, were now 'stranded on a reef at a height of 15 feet in the air'. This is one of the earliest reports of the pressure from big cliff-falls causing the nearby sea-bed to rise out of the water.

Inland are The Caves from which stone was mined for almost a century for the building of Exeter Cathedral, between 1275 and 1360, and later re-used for hiding smuggled contraband and occasional re-openings for ecclesiastical restorations. Modern open-pit workings are opposite.

Seaton Hole: only a strand of cliffs separate Seaton and Beer.

Axmouth port: a mile from the village.

9 BEER, SEATON and AXMOUTH

The last three communities on the Devon coast come in quick succession, each with its own valley, and can be explored in an afternoon from between Seaton and its Holiday Village (SY 247 902). Seaton and District Electric Tramway runs inland, along the course of the old branch railway to Kingsdon, midway to Seaton Junction which closed in 1966. The replacement rails for the tramway, opened in 1970, came from Sierra Leone.

St Gregory's parish church has the grave of smuggler Jack Rattenbury, born at Beer in 1778, who redeemed his reputation with tabloid-style memoirs.

Only the narrow White Cliff separates modern Seaton from Beer where a stream runs down the main street. It has the Anchor Inn and the Dolphin Inn. A Spanish Armada vessel is said to have enriched the local bloodline. Females used to be brought up at the loom in the production of Honiton lace.

Axmouth, the village, is further up the valley. The true Axe-mouth is immediately east of Seaton's otherwise undistinguished seafront. It retains a working wharf, buffered with car tyres, and a couple of characterful buildings between the tidal river and scrubby cliffs.

10 LANDSLIP NATIONAL NATURE RESERVE

The car-park in Seaton (SY 247 902) is also the closest point for reaching the western end of Landslip National Nature Reserve, managed by English Nature, which is below the coast path beyond Axmouth Bridge. This crosses the River Axe a short distance inland from its exceedingly narrow estuary. The 1877-dated bridge looks to be

Axmouth Bridge: moulded in Victorian concrete.

Shingle spit: providing a safe haven for Axe Yacht Club.

built of stone but is in fact a clever piece of moulded Victorian concrete. It confines Axmouth Yacht Club to a thin spit of shingle beside the funnel-like outlet into the sea.

Our onward route from the bridge skirts Axe Cliff Golf Course and then turns seawards from Barn Close Lane to Haven Cliff. The 6 miles of tumbling undercliff from here to Lyme Regis are managed by English Nature and contain colonies of rare orchids among the impenetrable scrub and badger tracks through carpets of wild garlic below tangles of ivy interwoven with wild clematis. Established in 1955, by what was then styled the Nature Conservancy, this pioneering reserve is a model of its kind and was among the first created under the National Parks and Access to the Countryside Act of 1949. It is as much a natural wilderness as anywhere on the South Coast and geological activity is at the core of its scientific interest. This spans the centuries and has brought the Jurassic to life in modern science.

Rev. W. D. Coneybeare and Professor William Buckland (1874-1856), both from Axminster, recorded the two great landslips of 26 December 1839 and 3 February 1840, with drawings by William Dawson. Buckland was the first to suggest, from comparisons with the action of ice on rocks in Switzerland, that much of northern England and Scotland had been under an ice-sheet. He had less success as a palaeontologist, advancing the Universal Deluge as the catastrophe theory to explain away fossils as drowned creatures left by the retreating waters of Noah's flood. It was a time when the Bibles still gave Archbishop James Ussher's 4004 BC date as the year when creation took place.

Subsidence between Axmouth and Lyme Regis was landform geology writ large and wide, with slippages of the blue lias clays having carried cottages and wheat fields seawards down the slope. It is still a dynamic landscape – liable to creeping reactivation – and path diversions and closures are to be expected. If the latter apply, then there is no alternative, other than to double back. This is seriously challenging country walking with nowhere to go other than to the towns at either end. For most of the time they are a long way off.

Dowlands Landslip started its greatest single move on Christmas Day in 1839. By Boxing Day some 20 acres of farmland had gone on their travels and left a ravine 300 metres wide and 150 metres deep. Seawards a reef rose 50 feet out of the water and the shoreline moved 500 metres into Lyme Bay. To the east, towards Whitlands, the thatched Annie's Cottage was left lurching at a tilt, halfway down the cliff. Its ruins are now not much more than a crumbling brick chimney-stack.

The other landmark is at the Lyme end of the nature reserve, above Underhill Farm, where a limestone outcrop called Chimney Rock used to have a fine view over The Cobb but is now almost totally engulfed in ivy, ash and sycamores. Underhill Farm became the home of novelist John Fowles and his first wife, Elizabeth, in the 1960s. A landslip persuaded them to move into the town, to Belmont House above The Cobb.

Below, left and right – *Dowlands Landslip: the cliffs started cracking at Christmas in 1839.*

This and the Landslip National Nature Reserve, provided the setting for his most famous book, *The French Lieutenant's Woman*, in 1969, which was filmed in both locations with Jeremy Irons and Meryl Streep.

Offshore, sunset coral forms a reef at a depth of 65 metres, three kilometres south of Lyme Regis. It was discovered in 1992 and is only the third that is known around Britain's coast, the others being in Plymouth Sound and off Lundy Island. The species is at the northern end of its range in the southern British Isles, being dependent upon warm water.

Nearby, known simply as 'The Wreck', the carcass of the 6000-ton freighter *Bay Gitano* provides one of the best fishing grounds along this coast. She was torpedoed by a German U-boat on 18 March 1918. Three of the crew were drowned but the rest were safely taken off by Lyme Lifeboat and the other small craft which came to the rescue of the sinking steamship. Much further out, the 15,000-ton battleship HMS *Formidable* was torpedoed at 02.20 hours on 1 January 1915, with the loss of 600 men.

11 WARE CLIFFS and DEVONSHIRE HEAD

National Trust ownership on the Dorset coast starts, appropriately, in Devon with a sliver of land on Devonshire Head which with the adjoining Ware Cliffs can be visited from Holmbush car-park at the top of Pound Street and Cobb Road in Lyme Regis (SY 337 920). These clifftop pastures form a 29-acre section of Ramscombe Farm which was bought in 1987 through an appeal launched by the novelist John Fowles and the Lyme Regis Society, supported by the Miss H. Howard bequest and the Nature Conservancy Council.

International author: John Fowles (left, with his gardener) brought Lyme new fame.

The Knap, the western clifftop field, has large hybridised dectylorchid colonies and sporadic bee orchids as well as the nearest cowslips to Lyme. There is also ragged robin and evening primrose. Stonechats breed here and butterflies occur in profusion. Bluebells smother the centre of the Trust's lands and badger tracks are evident across them, from setts in the coastal scrub.

Earthworks in the lower pasture to the east date from the nineteenth century and are the only surviving industrial archaeology related to Lyme Cement Works beside Monmouth Beach. Sluices and a dam held water, in an open reservoir, for heating the lias clays in the kilns below.

Eleanore Coade, who manufactured Regency terracotta mouldings, built Belmont House – now John Fowles's home – at the upper end of Cobb Road. She died in about

1820 and has been linked with the cement works though all the larger items that were given the firm's imprint proclaim 'COADE LAMBETH' and the business was based there, in London, at Pedlar's Acre.

Devonshire Head: from Monmouth Beach, where the Western Rebellion began.

12 MONMOUTH BEACH

The pebbles immediately west of The Cobb harbour at Lyme Regis, below Devonshire Head and the town's main Holmbush car-park (SY 337 920), saw one of the most ill-fated moments in English history. Here, in Poker's Pool, from a boat lowered from a Dutch ship anchored offshore, James Scott, Duke of Monmouth landed to proclaim himself King. He came ashore with 82 of his men on the evening of 11 June 1685. A green banner was unfurled with gold embroidered letters: 'Fear nothing but God.'

The party set off up 'the stile path', as Cobb Road was then, and the illegitimate son of Charles II proceeded to assemble a peasant army to challenge forces loyal to his uncle, James II. Monmouth fled from defeat at the last battle on English soil, from Sedgemoor in the Somerset Levels, on 6 July 1685. Captured on Horton Heath, near Ringwood, he was taken to the Tower of London and beheaded on Tower Hill.

Revenge upon Lyme Regis began on 11 September 1685 when George Jeffreys, 1st Baron Jeffreys of Wem and the Lord Chief Justice, visited Monmouth Beach to see the scaffold that had been prepared for the hanging the following day of a dozen victims from his Bloody Assize, most of whom were to be drawn and quartered so that their remains could be distributed for display to a wider public. Daniel Defoe had joined the rebels at Lyme and it was fortunate for him and English literature that he escaped the repercussions. He prudently remained coy about this episode for the rest of his life.

John Tutchin recorded in 1689 that 12 September 1685 was 'a glorious sun shining day'. It was seen as a 'kind of miracle' that two cart-horses refused to draw the sledge which was to have dragged the condemned men from the town. Then it was harnessed to a pair of coach-horses which 'broke it in pieces' and the men proceeded on foot.

First to die was Lieutenant-Colonel Abraham Holmes of the Civil War Parliamentary Army, retired, who had his arm shot to pieces in a skirmish at Norton St Philip. After this 'he laid it on a dresser, and cut it off himself with the cook-maid's knife'. Holmes 'was hanged on the very spot, where he landed with the Duke'.

Christopher Battiscombe was second. A young gentleman, his fiancée had gone on her knees to Judge Jeffreys and begged for him to be spared, to which Jeffreys is said to have replied: 'That he could only spare her part of him, but as he knew what she wanted, it should be the part which she liked best, and he would give orders to the sheriff accordingly.'

The third to suffer was William Hewling, aged twenty, from London, who had landed at Lyme with the Duke as a Lieutenant of Foot. His body, at least, was spared being butchered into sections for distribution around the West Country, as means of discouraging further rebellion: 'The maidens of Lyme, partly by assistance of the populace, and partly through the connivance of the persons in power, buried his remains in Lyme churchyard.'

Next it was the turn of Sampson Larke, a 'learned and dissenting teacher of Lyme', who was refused permission to make a speech. The guard interrupted him to point out that 'the work of the day was so great, they could not afford him time'.

Dr Benjamin Temple of Nottingham was, however, allowed his words. He had been engaged by the Duke of Monmouth in Holland as his physician and surgeon.

Sixth in line was Captain Arthur Matthews, a Captain of Foot, who forgave his executioner.

'Life, farewell, thou gaudy dream,' was part of the final utterances of Joseph Tyler, a gentleman poet from Bristol: 'Painted o'er with grief and joys, which the next short hour destroys.'

The eighth prisoner was William Cox, presumably from Lyme as he had the distinction of being the first man to enlist in the rebel army, after the Duke landed in the town.

Ninth to hang was Charmouth fisherman Samuel Robins who went on board the Duke's ship to sell fish and was then 'compelled to pilot him into Lyme'. It seems he would have been pardoned except that a copy of a seditious book, *The Solemn League and Covenant*, had been found at his house.

Nothing is known about the tenth victim, Josias Ascue.

Captain John Madders, Constable of Crewkerne, was another who was said to have almost escaped with his life. Someone then praised him at his trial as 'a good Protestant'. 'Oho!' says Jeffreys. 'He is a Presbyterian. I can smell them 40 miles. He shall be hanged.'

Finally came the turn of Captain John Kidd who had spent the whole day witnessing the 'dreadful sight' of the killing and dismembering of the 11 who had gone before.

Inland from Monmouth Beach and the Lifeboat Station stood Lyme Cement Works, with its chimneys set into Ware Cliffs, which produced stucco for decorative wall-facings. It also made hydraulic cement, designed to harden under water, as a specialised product for Victorian and Edwardian harbour-works. Lyme Cement Works was demolished early in the twentieth century.

Mary Anning: brought Lyme's fossils into the public domain.

THE NATURAL HISTORY MUSEUM, LONDON

13 LYME REGIS

Coram Towers, opposite the Holmbush car-park (SY 337 920) preserves the memory of Lyme's rich shipwright, Thomas Coram (1668-1751), who endowed London's Foundling Hospital and whose good works continues to this day, through the Thomas Coram Foundation. There is an impressive statue to him in Brunswick Square, London WC1.

The name most closely connected with Lyme's geology is that of Mary Anning (1799-1847) who is buried on the north side of the parish church. Her home, at the bottom of Broad Street, became the Fossil Depot. She is commemorated by a stained glass window in St Michael's Church: 'This window is sacred to the Memory of Mary Anning of this Parish, who died in the month of March, 1847, and is erected by the vicar of Lyme and some members of the Geological Society of London, in commemoration of her usefulness in furthering the Science of Geology, as also of her benevolence of heart and integrity of life.'

That says it all. The good women's 'usefulness' was in finding the specimens of Jurassic fauna that would make the reputation of others. They included the spectacular great dinosaurs, such as the remains of what we would call the ichthyosaur which was washed out of the cliffs by a storm in 1810, when she was eleven-years-old, and sold to occupant of Colway Manor for £23. It is now in the British Museum (Natural History) in South Kensington.

These were regarded as antediluvian creatures, the pre-Flood inhabitants of the Earth, that somehow failed to make it on to Noah's Ark. Judging from the fins, paddles, side-armour, and sheer size of what is left – plus bad breath in life – it would be quite logical to argue that they probably did not altogether appeal to Mrs Noah and were therefore left to fend for themselves in the flood.

'Fish-lizards' was about the best that early nineteenth-century pre-Darwin learning could make of them. In 1820 Mary Anning sold a splendidly preserved ichthyosaurus to the Duke of Buckingham for 120 guineas. Then in 1824 it was a perfect pterodactyl. They called it Diophodon.

Mary Anning would be remembered in Lyme Regis as an inoffensive little lady but that is pure sexism. She was assertive enough to tell the King of Saxony's physician: 'I am well known throughout the whole of Europe.' In fact the Germans always took more interest in fossils than the English, as they do to this day, and their interminable scientific arguments fascinated Miss Anning: 'I do so enjoy an opposition among the big wigs.'

Her great contemporary was the author Jane Austen, who lodged in Lyme in November 1803 and returned in September 1804, and immortalised the town in *Persuasion*. She is remembered on the ground with the Jane Austen Garden which was opened by Sir Hugh Smiley, chairman of the Jane Austen Society, in 1975. Many, like Tennyson, think of Lyme and Austen in the same breath: 'Don't talk to me of Monmouth, but show me the place where Louisa Musgrave fell.'

Those steps, projecting from The Cobb wall, remain an attraction and a hazard.

Francis Turner Palgrave (1824-97), the most eminent of Dorset's Victorian literati, settled at Little Park, Haye Lane, in 1872. His exhaustive anthologies included the Golden Treasury of the best Song and Lyrical Poems in the English Language.

The surgeon Joseph Lister, 1st Baron Lister of Lyme Regis (1827-1912), was the founder of antiseptic surgery. Influenced by the discoveries of Pasteur, he studied inflammation and suppuration of wounds, and used carbolic acid to prevent septic infection. The Lister family bought High Cliff at Lyme as a holiday home and Joseph's brother, Arthur Lister (1830-1908) made it his permanent residence. An expert on mosses, fungi and lichens, he was a world expert on small organisms called mycetozoa.

Royal doctor Sir Maurice Abbot-Anderson (1861-1938) retired to Madeira Cottage, in The Walk, in 1928. He founded Flora's League to campaign for the conservation of wild flowers. This work was carried on by his widow, Lady Muriel Abbot-Anderson (1888-1973), and their grave is carpeted by the daffodils she planted.

14 THE COBB

The mediaeval harbour at Lyme Regis is known as The Cobb (SY 339 915). It and Lyme, named for the nearby mouth of the River Lim, were synonymous for centuries. From 1279, when enfranchisement by Edward I brought it the Regis cachet, this was one of the premier ports of England. Earlier, salt-boiling was taking place, from 744 when the rights were granted to the Abbot of Sherborne, and 14 men were employed in the task after the Norman Conquest.

Fossil Depot: continued Mary Anning's business.

Micoderoceras birchi: *from the Lower Lias at Lyme Regis.*

High summer: the Cobb harbour with the Spittles in the background.

Slack water: the Cobb from Marine Parade, at low tide.

Shipping became the Lyme trade and grants and charters from Henry VIII and Elizabeth I centred on ensuring the continuing upkeep of The Cobb wall against its endless battering from the elements. Four Lyme vessels and 62 men sailed to join the siege of Calais in 1347. Two ships were fitted out and manned from Lyme for the English fleet that faced the Spanish Armada in 1588.

Lyme's maritime resources were rated at a sixth of that of the port of London. A garrison of 600 men and women at Lyme held the town for Parliament in the Civil War and resisted encirclement by a 5000-man force commanded by Prince Maurice of the Rhine.

Lyme declined and decayed as a port but by 1750 the fashionable set from Bath had discovered this seaside spa and Jane Austen's endorsement kept Lyme riding high into the next century. An engraving by George Cruikshank (1792-1878) that was published in London on 8 September 1819, and is on display in Lyme Regis Museum, shows bathing machines on the beach beside The Cobb. The ladies, as was the custom, are shown taking to the water without a costume between them. The title 'Hydromania! or a Touch of the Sub-Lyme and Beautiful' was satirical, being a comment both upon the unfathomable fashion for cold water and Edmund Burke's essay *On the Sublime and Beautiful*, published in 1756.

Regency style: thatch, stucco and lead drain-pipes, on Marine Parade.

Sea defences: seaward barriers beside the Lim estuary.

On 15 October 1825, Captain Sir Richard Spencer (1779-1838) of 6 Cobb Road, who had served under Lord Nelson, successfully experimented at The Cobb with the first self-buoyant lifeboat.

On the horizon off Lyme Regis you can frequently observe what may seem to be the mating habits of oil tankers. Here the huge vessels from the Gulf twin-up with a lesser breed. 'Lightening' is the term given to the partial unloading of crude oil from supertankers in excess of 250,000 tonnes into smaller vessels. This causes the big ships to rise sufficiently in the water to enable them to enter British estuaries. The procedure was pioneered by Shell in about 1970, with Lyme Bay being chosen because it is protected by the projecting coasts of Start Point and Portland, to offer the most sheltered water in the approaches to Britain from the south-west.

The Buddle: where the River Lim flows into the sea.

15 THE SPITTLES

The old road from the corner midway up Timber Hill (SY 345 932) used to continue across the cliffs from Lyme Regis to Charmouth, and now provides a parking area beside the National Trust gate and signs. In 1901 these shale cliffs sparked off the last and most determined of the attempts to discover a Dorset coalfield. A syndicate

Next bay: Spittles and Black Ven from Church Cliffs.

Warning signs: landslips resume on Lyme's eastern front.

Active mudflow: the Spittles opening up, with Lyme Regis beyond.

ignored geological advice and commissioned a team of South Wales engineers to bore 400 metres before giving up. They had expected to find a coal seam at 200 metres. This was the deepest hole in Dorset until the onset of oil exploration.

Lyme had a burning cliff in 1908. Known as 'The Lyme Volcano' it came about from spontaneous combustion through oxidation of pyrite, which contains 53 per cent sulphur, with the oil shale. The fire smouldered for years but cynics claimed that hoteliers surreptitiously paid for cart-loads of coal to be delivered to the local tourist attraction.

The coast road to Charmouth headed north-east across The Spittles until being carried away by a series of landslips in the 1920s. These continued through the century, with the eastern side being carried across the Canary Ledges and into the sea by mudflows in 1959 and the winter of 1969-70. Other parts of the cliff have edged towards the sea in recent years as rainfall seeps down through the chert and greensand top layers and causes these to slide off the underlying Liassic clays.

A total of 126 acres of cracking meadows and scrubby landslipped undercliff were bought by the National Trust, through its Enterprise Neptune appeal, in 1974. 'The Spittles' sounds so descriptive as the placename for a dynamic landscape spat out from the cliff, but research only yields 'spittle', in middle English, for land on which a hospital was built – unlikely in this case – or land owned by a hospital.

16 BLACK VEN and DEVIL'S BELLOWS

The cliffs west of Charmouth are reached by a former coach-road heading straight into a wilderness, literally dropping into a chasm on National Trust land at the bottom of Old Lyme Hill (SY 357 933). Its continued repair across the mudslides of the Devil's Bellows became impossible in the 1920s and it is now abandoned amid the tumbling scrub where a century earlier fossil hunter Mary Anning found dinosaur bones and extracted her ichthyosaurus. A 3-metre long herbivorous armoured-plated dinosaur is a species known only from Black Ven and wood-stone nodules yield fossil wood.

Black Ven had become reliably dynamic. Subsequent landslides took away Higher Sea Lane in the 'mud glacier' of 1938. Repeat performances in 1957-58 and 1969-70 pulled apart the last ongoing remains of the alternative road to Lyme. The section from Foxley Ridge is engulfed in the undercliff.

Then a mountainous section of cliff slid down from the 477-feet contour and oozed out to sea in 1969. It covered Canary Ledges but has since hardened and is now itself suffering serious erosion. By 1986 it was half of what had been washed away by the waves. The upper terraces failed again in 1994 when a mud-slide took three minutes to crash down from the golf course to the sea. Trees rode the avalanche as a school group stood in amazement having only left the path of the mudflow half an hour before.

Activitiy resumed at Black Ven in the prolonged rains of 2000 when there was more than a mile of moving cliffs between Lyme Regis and Golden Cap.

National Trust ownership of 49 acres at Black Ven was largely achieved with Enterprise Neptune funds between 1966 and 1968 with additional land being bought through a legacy from Miss E. F. R. Nicholls and Miss E. B. I. Nicholls in 1973. Mr F. W. Miers gave an extra piece of land in 1987.

Mixed messages: award winning dangers at Charmouth.

17 CHARMOUTH

Twentieth-century fossil finding moved eastwards from Lyme Regis to Charmouth is now based around Charmouth Heritage Centre (SY 365 931). Whereas the nineteenth-century cliffside exposures on the other side of Lyme were becoming a tangle of impenetrable vegetation, the new 'mud glacier' beside Charmouth village pulled ammonites and dinosaur fossils out of the cliff, and conveniently dumped them across the beach. Other mudflows and mudslides, threatening the very existence of the village, brought a succession of fresh exposures of the inhabitants in

Charmouth: dammed by the shingle beach, through which it trickles.

and beside the former warm-water sea which had been both muddy and shallow in Jurassic times.

Conveniently, for modern geologists, it had an anaerobic bottom which provided optimum conditions for decomposition into a state of preservation rather than facilitating the much more usual re-cycling of carcasses by other creatures. The remains of its animals therefore tend to be intact, rather than half-eaten and strewn around, and can sometimes be reassembled.

Finding them in time is another matter, before erosion and the sea destroys the fossils, but keen eyes and foul weather make for efficient fossil collecting. Landslips bring treasures on to the beach where they are washed out of the mud by rain and waves. 'There is nothing we like more than a hurricane,' I was told by a collector. 'January is the best month because there's then a succession of storms and we can work without having to compete with the grockles.'

Finds are taken to the Heritage Centre for evaluation. The deal with the collectors and dealers is that the finder can be keeper, without any question arising from legal title to the ground, provided that fossils can be recorded and graded with the first option for purchase of rarities being given to British museums. Persuading them to raise the necessary funds is another matter but a number of outstanding finds have been saved over the years and are now on public display across the country.

Charmouth's shingle beach is remembered for the ill-fated canoe adventure into Lyme Bay which set off into worsening weather at 10.05 hours on 20 March 1993. The ordeal ended at 18.44 hours when a Sea King helicopter picked up the last member of the party of two instructors, a teacher, and eight Plymouth sixth-formers. Four of the teenagers were dead and school trips would never be quite the same again as issues of responsibility and safety were brought under the media and legal spotlight.

Much of the present bank of shingle came down the valley, with a collection of caravans, in the flash-flood of 1979. Perhaps the least-known Charmouth resident is *Cochlicella barbara*. This rare salt-water snail has only two known British colonies; in marshland here beside the River Char and at a similar site near Torquay.

The Queen's Arms in The Street (SY 365 937) is named for Catherine of Aragon who stayed here in 1501. She was followed a century-and-a-half later by Charles II, incognito, as he fled from defeat at the Battle of Worcester.

18 STONEBARROW DOWN and CAIN'S FOLLY

The track up Stonebarrow Lane, from Newlands Hotel, Charmouth, to the informal parking area on the 500-feet plateau of Stonebarrow Down (SY 385 934) used to be the main road from Charmouth to Morcombelake until it was replaced by the turnpike to the north in 1824. The Stonebarrow Down section of the old Dorchester to Exeter coach-road seems to be on the course of the 'lost' Roman road between the two towns.

Cain's Folly: Charmouth's eastern cliffs, towards Golden Cap.

As with so much of this coast, landslips have both removed and revealed historic features, with a wartime RAF radar station having slipped down the cliff at Cain's Folly on 14 May 1942. The crew are said to have stepped out unhurt as the concrete building came to a halt at the bottom. The slippage also carried off the beach clump which carried the Cain's Folly name. Other parts collapsed in 1877 and the cliff edge has receded by 125 metres since the 1860s though the net loss to the sea has been only 35 metres as the undercliff has expanded to more than half a mile in width.

One of the largest fossil skeletons ever found in Britain of an ichthyosaur, a dolphin-like dinosaur which lived on cuttlefish and squid, was discovered in the late 1980s on the cliffs between Charmouth and Stanton St Gabriel. It comprised a 6-metre body section but 2 metres of tail. It has a pointed stout, razor-like teeth, and a series of what seem to have been movable plates along the top of its backbone.

The creature had sunk into the limey mud of the shallow sub-tropical Lower Jurassic sea about 200 million years ago and reappeared as bands of what are now blue lias shale and limestone eroded at the cliff-edge. The National Heritage Memorial Fund made a grant of £8000 to help Bristol Museum and Art Gallery acquire this important specimen in 1989.

Between Stonebarrow Hill and Westhay Farm, in the corner of Monument Coppice, stands a 2-metre high obelisk: 'This stone marks the spot where Robert Henry Hildyard Esquire fell dead whilst out shooting, September 16th 1876, aged 40. He was 2nd Secretary in H. M. Diplomatic Service. Lord of the Manor of Catherston and J. P. for the County. He was the only child of his mother and she was a widow.'

Stonebarrow Hill, Cains Folly and Westhay Farm comprise 366 acres and include the starting point for the National Trust's Golden Cap Estate, which was given in 1961 in memory of Oliver Morland. Additions were made between 1966 and 1981.

19 STANTON ST GABRIEL

At the centre of the time-warp coastal parish of Stanton St Gabriel is the lias-stone ruin of its thirteenth-century church, and traces of a 'lost' village (SY 402 924) in an ancient pastoral landscape almost entirely owned by the National Trust. The surviving thatched cottage and farmhouse used to be part of a dense cluster of buildings in the valley beneath Golden Cap. In 1650 there were 23 families living around the green.

After the French Wars the church, where services were last held before 1800, was 'frequently used as a receiving house for smuggled kegs of brandy'. Another of the tales attached to this dangerous coast concerns what would have been the loss of life in an imminent shipwreck on a stormy night inn 1872 which was averted by what Charmouth people believe to have been a divine premonition. Isaac Hunter, a Charmouth fisherman, had a violent dream brought on 'by anxiety for his lobster pots'. He was in such a distressed state that he immediately dressed and set off to run eastwards along the coast, for 3 kilometres, in the teeth of a gale.

He found a French ship in distress, off Golden Cap, and was able to raise the Coastguard and effect the successful rescue of the ship's crew. The vessel became a total wreck.

Smuggling hideaway: the last recorded use for St Gabriel's Church.

Small fields and dense hedgerows, tall and overhanging, typify a nineteenth-century mixed farming landscape. These days it is almost totally pastoral with lush herb-rich meadows on a clay soil. Some of the hedges reached house-height in 1985 though they were then cut and laid. Nowhere else in Dorset is an unimproved landscape still being farmed on this scale.

A total of 444 acres of St Gabriels, Filcombe and Norchard Farms were bought by the Trust between 1967 and 1972 with Enterprise Neptune funds and legacies from Miss Jessie McNab, R. I. Gunn and Miss Gwendolen Pelly. Inland, towards Stonebarrow Hill, 405 acres of Chardown Hill and Upcot Farm had been acquired through Enterprise Neptune in 1966.

20 GOLDEN CAP

The highest cliff on the South Coast of England, Golden Cap is reached from inland across the fields from a National Trust car-park in Langdon Wood (SY 412 931). This is found by turning south into Muddyford Lane from the A35 at the top of Chideock Hill, between Morcombelake and Chideock, and following a track upwards into the pines.

Golden Cap: from across a consolidated Broom Cliff landslip.

Inland approach: the path up Golden Cap from Langdon Hill.

Named for its sandy upper parts, which not only catch the light but can remain surprisingly conspicuous even in poor weather, 188-metre Golden Cap outdoes Beachy Head and dominates the valleys of Stanton St Gabriel and Seatown, as well as the entire wider panorama of Lyme Bay.

The underlying geology of Golden Cap is Lower Lias of the Jurassic with a golden crown of Cretaceous sand. The sequence from the beach upwards is belemnite marls and then green ammonite beds of the Lower Lias. Then three tiers of the Middle Lias are separated first by the Eype nodule bed and then a starfish bed. The yellow greensand of the Cretaceous is topped with a thin bed of chert.

Two ancient burial mounds on the plateau are just over 1 metre in height and date from about 1600 BC in the Bronze Age. The summit and heather-covered slopes cover 26 acres. A block of Purbeck stone has an inset slate plaque commemorating their acquisition as the hub of the estate taking its name: 'Golden Cap. Given by members of the National Trust and friends in memory of the Earl of Antrim KBE, Chairman of the National Trust from 1966 until his death in 1977.'

On the back of the boulder, which was brought to the summit in the scoop of a bulldozer in 1978, is a fossil cast. Prominent in the upper seaward corner it was part of

Yellow greensand: distinctive topping for the highest cliff on the South Coast.

Western view: National Trust cliffs all the way to Lyme.

the matrix of a big ammonite. This is particularly apposite. For the ashes of Bradford Abbas geologist and palaeontologist Sidney Savory Buckman (1860-1929) were scattered from Golden Cap. His pioneering work from the quarries around Sherborne showed how fossils could be used to date the rocks from which they had been taken.

The golden parts of the cliff are a yellow layer of fine sand, foxmould, which is the upper greensand of the Lower Cretaceous period. This contrasts with the underlying dark clays. An extensive seascape is visible from the top, from Start Point around to Portland Bill, and there is a breathtaking view down to the inshore waters. Landslipped debris and mudslides have carried a ribbon of rocks into the sea. They are known, from east to west, as The Corner, Cann Harbour, The Cove, and the Western Patches. It is one of the classic examples of landform geology on the Dorset coast.

Eight acres of The Saddle, forming a col between Golden Cap and Langdon Wood, were bought by the Trust in 1968.

21 SEATOWN and CHIDEOCK

There is a real anchor beside the Anchor Inn at Seatown hamlet, less than a kilometre seawards from the A35 at Chideock (SY 421 918). It is 4 metre-long, rusty and pebble-encrusted, from the 350-ton, 30-gun Dutch treasure ship Hope which was wrecked on the Chesil Beach, opposite Fleet, on the night of 16 January 1748. The anchor was found 75 metres off the Chesil Beach, by West Bay fisherman Jack Woolmington, in September 1986, and sold to publican David Miles.

Seatown countryside: across the valley to Doghouse Hill and Thorncombe Beacon.

Seatown beach saw the first landing of the Duke of Monmouth rebels, on the morning of 11 June 1685, when two men rowed ashore. An English gentleman, Thomas Dare, was accompanied by Andrew, Lord Fletcher. The latter, a fiery Scot, was second-in-command of the Duke's cavalry. The two slipped into Dorset as the advance party to organise the imminent attempt at seizing the throne for Monmouth, from his uncle, James II.

Their exploits charted a course for failure that would be consistent with the expedition as a whole. Fletcher pulled rank to commandeer Dare's horse. The Englishman refused and raised his whip; at which Fletcher shot him through the head.

Volunteers who witnessed the incident wanted Fletcher strung up for murder but he was smuggled back aboard ship and escaped to Spain. Nonetheless it was a disastrous own-goal for Monmouth's side. Fletcher could have been invaluable – an aggressive Scot was just what Monmouth lacked at the head of his hesitant horsemen for the coming skirmish at Bridport and the rout at the Battle of Sedgemoor. Thomas Dare also had a vital position as paymaster for the operation.

Rev. C. V. Goddard, the vicar of Chideock in the 1890s, recorded smuggling tales from Seatown. Rev. T. Worthington, a curate in the 1880, also wrote of the scale of the local

Below left – *Seatown beach: between Golden Cap and Ridge Cliff, with Burton Cliff beyond.* Below – *Seatown hamlet: clusters around the Anchor Inn.*

Seatown shadows: with the hamlet dwarfed by Golden Cap.

free-trading: 'Within the memory of some of the inhabitants there used to be 30 to 40 fishermen at Seatown, ostensibly employed in their lawful avocations, but really in smuggling. Not the fishermen only, but as in other seaside places half a century ago, the inhabitants in general were implicated in this contraband traffic, of which the sin, in their eyes, consisted only in being found out. Numerous stories are told of hair-breadth escapes from the clutches of the Excise officers.'

Inland, two great jaw-bones that rise 3 metres above a garden gate at Chideock Manor comprise one of only 30 such arches in Great Britain that are still complete. These bones were taken from an animal washed up at Seatown by lord of the manor Sir Charles Weld in 1880. It is the only whalebone arch in Dorset.

The River Winniford runs under a humped and cobbled packhorse bridge at Seatown and flows through the shingle into the sea. The Watch-House is the Victorian Coastguard Station. Into recent times the beach was being removed for aggregates, until it was eventually recognized that this was indeed a finite resource, not being replenished by the sea at night.

Onwards and upwards in either direction, each way for three or four kilometres, the entire coast is owned by the National Trust. West Cliff is dominated by Golden Cap. Ridge Cliff is dominant to west, being part of 195 acres bought in 1966 through an anonymous donation to Enterprise Neptune. Another 76 acres towards Chideock were acquired in 1994. The next section of cliff towards Thorncombe Beacon is Doghouse Hill where 70 acres were bought by the Trust in 1967 with a bequest from Miss Marian Howard and a Nature Conservancy grant.

22 THORNCOMBE BEACON and DOWNHOUSE FARM

The second of the twin peaks of Lyme Bay, 507-feet Thorncombe Beacon is 3 kilometres east of Golden Cap, and best reached from Eype Mouth (SY 448 911). It belongs to the Middle Lias period. Three Bronze Age burial mounds include one of the largest bowl barrows along this stretch of coast. The name of the headland and a replica Armada-period fire bucket confirm that this was the crucial beacon for Lyme Bay, rather than being placed on the higher Golden Cap as is sometimes assumed. Thorncombe Beacon was a more practical location given its easier plateau-like approach from Eype Down. The most recent layer of history has been lost, with a 1940-built pillbox and bunker having been blown up by Royal Engineers, in the 1970s.

Thorncombe Beacon was part of the 176-acre Down House Farm, towards Eype Down, which was given to the National Trust by playwright Robert Cedric Sherriff

Clockwise, starting from top left – *Doghouse Hill: western foothills of Thorncombe Beacon, above East Ebb Cove.*
Eastern undercliff: to Eype and West Bay, emerging from the shadows.
Sandy undercliff: westwards from Thorncombe Beacon to Doghouse Hill.
Armada replica: fire-bucket on Thorncombe Beacon.

Colmer's Hill: pine-topped in an oriental way.

(1896-1975) in 1966. He lived behind the trees on the leeward slope. R. C. Sherriff's first performance, in aid of a school chapel appeal fund in 1921, led to a professional career that opened with *Journey's End* being produced at the Savoy Theatre. Films now needed words and he established his reputation as a dramatist with *The Invisible Man* and *Goodbye Mr Chips*. He last epic script would be *The Dam Busters* from Paul Brickhill's narrative of the legendary exploits of Guy Gibson VC and the Lancasters of 617 Squadron. From above Down House Farm the view across the scrubbed-up common land of Eype Down is to Colmer's Hill. This perfect cone is topped by stylised pines, etched on the skyline, in the style of a chinese painting. It is otherwise unwooded but owned by the Woodland Trust.

23 EYPE MOUTH

My favourite quirky story of Eype Mouth (SY 448 911) concerns Cliff Close which briefly witnessed the last sighting of Malmesbury's Member of the Parliament, Walter Powell, who was whisked away into the sky on 10 December 1881. He had failed to jump clear of the War Office balloon *Saladin*, on secondment to the Meteorological Society, which then drifted out of control, over Lyme Bay. Its remains, though without those of the MP, were found on a Spanish mountain.

Right – *Coast path: to Eype Mouth and Thorncombe Beacon.* Far right – *Cracked cliff: carrying off the path between Eype Mouth and West Bay.*

Wartime anti-invasion pillboxes survive around Eype which is pronounced 'Eep'. Eype's Mouth Hotel and a number of idyllic golden-stone cottages, with masses of flowering shrubs, nestle beside the narrow cul-de-sac lanes of Lower Eype. One, a former Post Office, is named *Journey's End* in tribute to the work of that name by playwright R. C. Sherriff. As well as his former farm the National Trust also owns 18 acres of pasture which was acquired through Enterprise Neptune in 1994. The coast path in the other direction rises across a quarried hill beside the remains of a limekiln as it heads towards West Bay.

The greyish cliffs to West Bay are of Forest marble and Fuller's earth. E. C. H. Day discovered a 'curious and persistent layer of small nodules' at the foot of the cliff west of Eype Mouth, in 1863. They contain ammonite fragments.

24 WEST BAY and BRIDPORT HARBOUR

The historic Bridport Harbour lies behind double piers, between which a channel carries the River Brit into Lyme Bay, in what is now the holiday resort of West Bay (SY 465 904). The harbour has been rebuilt through the ages after a succession of storms and floods. Shipbuilding was the major occupation in the creek between the Waterworks and the Salt House, on Pitfield Marsh, until Elias Cox's time in the late nineteenth century. The 1002-ton *Speedy*, built for the Australia run, was the biggest

Pier Terrace: conspicuous backdrop to Bridport Harbour.

Harbour Museum: the cannon haul is from shipwrecks.

vessel to be launched there, in 1853. She, like so many other British naval and cargo ships, was fitted out with cordage made in Bridport town.

Rope-making remains a local industry though no one has been 'stabbed with a Bridport dagger' since the abolition of capital punishment. West Bay, meanwhile, evolved rather late in the cycle of seaside fashionableness. It relied upon an extension of the branch railway from the town, in 1884, when its largest building was the Coastguard Station, until completion of Pier Terrace, otherwise known as Noah's Ark, which was designed by E. S. Prior with a distinctive hip-roof in 1885 and now incorporates the Bay House Hotel.

The thatched Bridport Arms Hotel stands beside the shingle beach and on the other side of the harbour, where chalets and caravans now cover the former shipyard, the Esplanade was built by Thomas Colfax in 1897 to celebrate Queen Victoria's Golden Jubilee. The sea defences were revamped in 1969 but the threat came from behind in 1974 when a combination of river and tide flooded much of the town.

Right – *Feeding time: on the Brit estuary, opposite the George Hotel* Far right – *East Cliff: banded layers of the Bridport sands, from the harbour entrance.*

25 FRESHWATER and BURTON CLIFF

The vertical banded cliffs of golden Bridport sands, alternating with nodules of calcareous sandstone rock, give a glorious change of colour to the two miles of coast west from Southover at Burton Bradstock (SY 491 889). The sequence begins with East Cliff, overlooking West Bay, with a golf course on top where a denuded Bronze Age burial mound has yielded a stone with cup-and-ring marks which are a rarity in a Dorset context.

Freshwater, named for the River Bride which disappears into the seaside pebbles, has an extensive holiday camp which was among the many such facilities occupied in 1943 by the 1st Infantry Division of the United States Army. They departed from Weymouth and Portland on 6 June 1944 to take 'Bloody Omaha' in the fiercest fighting on D-Day. They had taken part in a realistic training exercise when Assault Landing Craft came up the beach and fired batteries of rockets that trailed rope-ladders from the top of Burton Cliff. Troops then landed from another wave of assault vessels and scaled them in a successful rehearsal for the invasion of Normandy.

Layered strata: forming alternate columns and buttresses.

Southover: the beach-side extremity of Burton Bradstock, between National Trust fields.

William Crowe's poem *Lewesdon Hill* of 1788 contains a allusion to 'Burton, and thy lofty cliff, where oft the mighty blaze is kindled'. A footnote to the first edition explains the reference: 'The cliff is among the loftiest of all upon that coast and smugglers often take advantage of its height for the purpose related in the poem.'

These sheer 100-feet cliffs rise from a wide beach and gritty shingle. Hilltop pastures tilt inland towards the village of Burton Bradstock which shelters in the Bride valley. National Trust ownership of a mile of cliffs, half of it inland as far as the B3157 coast road, includes the prehistoric Bind Barrow to the east of Southover. The Trust owns a total of 102 acres, acquired between 1967 and 1990 through a gift from Miss Edith M. Adlard and Miss M. B. Clark, bequests from Miss T. M. Edmondson and Miss M. A. Jacobsen, Enterprise Neptune funds and a Nature Conservancy grant.

26 THE OTHONA COMMUNITY

On the south side of the B3157 between Burton Bradstock and Swyre, stands Community House which is a religious retreat for the Othona Community (SY 511 883). Formerly known as St Bride's Farm, it was established by Adela Curtis (1864-1960), the Japanese-born author of *Janardana* in 1905 and *The New Mysticism* in 1907. She put her ideas into practice in 1912 with the Order of Silence, a community she founded at Coldash, Berkshire. More converts were won over by *Creative Silence* in 1920. This was sub-titled as a manual of meditation for beginners in the practice of bodily transmutation.

In the 1920s, Miss Curtis brought her celibate and contemplative vegetarian Christian commune – which was exclusively female – to the Dorset coast. They worked the land around the newly-built St Bride's Farm and villagers knew them as 'The White Ladies' because of their creamy veils and robes. White Ladies survives as a house name.

A large chapel was built beside the farm and opened in 1938. They had become the Christian Contemplatives' Community and evolved a strict set of rules. Papists and Christian Scientists were excluded from membership. Electricity and piped water were banned. Sewage was to be collected for use on the fields as the natural basis for the organic growth of produce. The day would have seven set periods of contemplation, starting at 05.00 hours.

Adela Curtis urged others to adopt 'the power of prayer' as a wartime weapon against Adolf Hitler. These incantations were personalised against the specific target and rendered as a repetitive chant. They were answered, perhaps, by his suicidal decision to invade Russia instead.

Miss Curtis never quite reached her century. She died on 17 September 1960 and has her memorial in the chapel: 'I have loved thee with an everlasting love.'

Her end would have caused her to curse on three counts of commission and omission. Being cremated, at Weymouth, offended against her beliefs as she disapproved of the use of gas. She had wished for herself, as she urged for all natural wastes, to be returned to the soil on the land where she toiled. The Othona Community took over St Bride's Farm, bringing a more relaxed regime, about which she would also have had her opinions.

27 COGDEN BEACH and BURTON MERE

Community House overlooks the next stretch of National Trust coastline, which begins after a 250-metre gap beside the Old Coastguard House and then extends for a 1½ kilometres, reached from a car-park on the south side of the B3157 a mile east of Burton Bradstock (SY 504 883). These grassland slopes towards Lyme Bay include Cliff End towards the western end and lack any cliffs further east. Instead, as the coast path heads towards Abbotsbury, the land gradually levels out towards the sea after Cogden Beach and the reed-beds and water of Burton Mere are sandwiched between the shingle and the pastures. Avian residents have to cope with walkers on both sides of the lagoon. Some choose the beach, logically enough, but for no good reason the legal line of the coast path is on the inland side of Burton Mere.

Below left – *Caravan country: sandwiched between National Trust pastures.* Below – *Cogden Beach: from Cliff End to West Bexington.*

Man Friday: an angler's deep footsteps in Cogden Beach.

Mackerel are the traditional mass-catch fish along this shore. Changing sea temperatures and offshore over-fishing affect the size and frequency of shoals but seine-netting, from off the Chesil Beach between Burton Bradstock and Langton Herring, can still bring fish ashore in quantity. There is also a leisure industry of beach anglers and fishing parties in boats. Traditionally, as Thomas Gerard recorded in the 1620s, fishing was 'the chiefest trade' of the Abbotsbury people. Daniel Defoe found 'all the way on the seashore' there were 'ships fishing for mackerel' in 1724.

Cogden Beach is effectively the western end of the Chesil Beach which extends south-eastwards in a widening sweep all the way to Portland. The Trust owns a total of 258 acres at Cogden and above Burton Mere, acquired in 1994 with bequests from Mrs Mary Shafer and Lady Isla Twysden, Neptune funds, and grants from the Countryside Commission and Dorset local authorities.

28 WEST BEXINGTON

The hamlet of West Bexington has a bungalow where in the Cold War you could have observed Royal Navy officers with binoculars watching our submarines surfacing in Lyme Bay, and its seaside dwellings were still making news in 2002, when a beach hut sold for £120,000 (SY 532 865). The Old Manor Hotel is further up the slope. Silhouetted on the escarpment above, towards Puncknowle – called 'Punnel' locally – the Lookout on The Knoll has Coastguard and smuggling associations, plus a wartime pillbox set into its seaward side.

Further east, above Labour-in-Vain Farm there is a limekiln which has been splendidly restored by the National Trust. It is open to view from the top, with an iron grill inset above the circular cavern, and a spring now issues out of the bottom. Above are the humps and hollows of an extensive quarry. The hilltop is also studded with Bronze Age burial mounds.

Below, the shingle widens into what is now visibly part of the Chesil Beach. Pink thrift and white campion clumps on the landward side and the pebbles spread on to an undulating track. Burton Road retains its status as a public road and runs beside the beach for two miles. The first 1½ kilometres are National Trust land. A total of 262 acres include the scrubby ridge given by Sir Ronald Milne Watson in 1964, rough grazing bought through a donation from Mrs Ella Corbett, and Labour-in-Vain Farm which was received in lieu of death duties and transferred from the Treasury to the Trust in 1979.

Beyond the Trust's coastline, Burton Road passes Greenbanks and the Essex-style clapper-boarded Old Coastguards. It was the home of literary journalist Henry Major

The Knoll: coastal lookout between Bexington and Puncknowle.

Tomlinson (1873-1958) in 1927 when he was proof-reading his novel *Gallion's Reach*. In the early 1930s he built his own house, on a plot sold-off by the nearby Labour-in-Vain Farm, and called this Gallion's Reach.

East Bexington Farm and Lawrence's Cottage are next, along with more pillboxes from the defences against Hitler's proposed Operation Sealion in the summer of 1940.

New Coastguards, alternatively known as Castle Hill Cottages, incorporates one of the most remarkable pillboxes in the country. Camouflaging this machine-gun position was achieved by disguising it as part of the kitchen at the western end of the building. It only shows up now from its soft twentieth-century bricks inserted into hard Victorian walls.

Castle Farm is followed by the hilltop remnants of Strangways Castle or Abbotsbury Castle; not to be confused with the hill-fort of the same name. This was the opulent seaside villa of the Earls of Ilchester, built in 1720 by Elizabeth, the 1st Countess of Ilchester. In 1791 the 2nd Earl erected a fashionable bathing-house on the beach below the castle, complete with dressing room and hot and cold baths.

Strangways Castle was gutted by fire in a gale in February 1913. Rebuilding was carried out, in 1916, but the replacement was demolished in 1934. A public path crosses the site.

New Coastguards: incorporates a wartime pillbox (below the bay window).

Abbotsbury Castle: the Iron Age hill-fort overlooking Lyme Bay.

29 ABBOTSBURY SUB-TROPICAL GARDENS

The famous Sub-Tropical Gardens started life as an extension of the grounds of Abbotsbury Castle, where generations of the Ilchester family and botanical explorers planted a multitude of rarities, in the mild micro-climate of a lush valley secreted a kilometre inland from the windswept Chesil Beach (SY 563 849). An olive tree flourished for many years until it succumbed to the cold winter of 1838-39. Camellias from China and Japan cover ten acres, some growing to tree size, and flower from February to May. The Sikkim and Himalayan rhododendrons achieve great size and also have large flowers. Indian azaleas were used as the basic border shrub.

Pampas grass: exotic hedge beside the lane to the Sub-Tropical Gardens.

Eucalypts from Australia were flowering and producing fertile seed by the 1860s. Figs also fruit well, as they do in Abbotsbury village, and now more generally along our Jurassic Coast. Fan palms manage an impressive size, as do Mexican yuccas, and cork trees from Spain. In the damper parts there are forests of Chinese bamboo and giant-leaf *Gunnera manicata* from the jungles of Brazil.

The walled garden is particularly delightful, especially in May when the Pacific dogwood, *Cornus nuttallii* from California, is smothered with giant white 'flowers', which are actually the bracts. Towards the sea there is a glade with a cemetery of pets of the Ilchester household and some old cannon. Pea fowl add a touch of elegance, particularly when the cocks fan their tails.

The garden grows is own replacement stock, to maintain the genetic purity of early introductions, and there is a small plant centre offering surplus stock for sale. Abutilon, which is covered with attractive blue flowers for three months, is suitable for a sunny position in a garden of any size. More exotic, with fleshy evergreen leaves that resemble rusty hacksaw blades is *Pseudopanax crassifolious* from New Zealand, but it tends to suffer from frost in southern English suburbs.

30 ST CATHERINE'S CHAPEL

The prominent landmark of the Abbotsbury coast is St Catherine's Chapel, standing at 275 feet on an oval platform at the top of Chapel Hill (SY 573 848). It is reached by a 750 metre path, uphill across mediaeval strip lynchets, from just west of the Ilchester Arms Hotel in Abbotsbury village. Part of Abbotsbury Abbey, the chapel dates from the late fourteenth century, and was the only building to survive

Chapel view: from Abbotsbury Hill, to the Chesil Beach and Portland.

intact after the ousting of the Benedictine community in 1539. Retained as a sea-mark, repairs were made in 1742, and the fine barrel-shaped ceiling was restored in the 1970s. Renovations were carried out in bright yellow local stone to match the original fabric.

Spiral stairs lead to the octagonal turret beside the roof. A door opens on to a balcony, around the side of the roof, which was used for a sea-watch. Apart from the door the building is without any timbers.

St Catherine, the patron saint of spinsters, was a frequent choice for high-place dedications. Single women prayed here: 'For a husband, St Catherine. A handsome one, St Catherine. A rich one, St Catherine. A nice one, St Catherine. And soon, St Catherine.'

31 CHESIL BEACH

The last car-park beside the Chesil Beach for 14 kilometres, on the Isle of Portland, is at the end of Cleverlawns which turns seawards from the B3157 west of Abbotsbury and passes the Sub-Tropical Gardens (SY 560 846). From this beach, in 1964, the ashes of the Dorset novelist John Cowper Powys (1872-1964) were cast into the waves, with this spot being chosen because he used the treacherous shingle bank for the shipwreck scene in *Weymouth Sands*.

'All the people of Abbotsbury, including even the vicar, are thieves, smugglers, and plunderers of shipwrecks,' a pamphleteer wrote during the mysterious case of Elizabeth Canning's disappearance in 1752, though there is also evidence that they indulged in legitimate maritime activity.

The greatest mackerel catch on record for Dorset took place between Abbotsbury and Bexington in June 1764: 'Such a quantity of mackerel was caught at Abbotsbury as the oldest man living don't remember. There were drawn on shore, by twice shooting seine-nets, at least 200,000 fish. Thousands of these are still on the beach, there not being sufficient people to carry them away.'

Abbotsbury's annual pagan survival, held on 13 May which preserved the May Day of the pre-1722 calendar, took place here when flower-covered structures were brought on poles after having been paraded around the village. Games and festivities had their origin in a deeper fertility cult. All the village took part and the garlands were finally placed in fishing boats and rowed out to sea where they were cast overboard to drift on the waves.

Chesil Beach: the pebble ridge from Abbotsbury to Portland.

Abbotsbury village: with Chesil Beach beyond, from White Hill.

Sometimes, off Abbotsbury, a boat would fail to catch any fish even though there might be great shoals all around and other boats in the party would be hauling full nets on to the shingle. The unlucky boat would be considered bewitched. This spell was considered to be broken by an act of sympathetic magic in which a mackerel was attached to the rudder and then liberally stuck with pins.

South-eastwards, the beach is crossed by a parallel rows of immense concrete cubes, erected as Dragon's Teeth anti-tank obstacles against threatened invasion by the Wehrmacht's Army Group B under General Field-Marshal Fedor von Bock in 1940.

Omolphur rufitarus is 1½ centimetres long and one of Britain's rarest beetles. It is believed to feed on pollen of the thrift flower, *Armeria maritima*, but only in limited locations such as in the vicinity of the Dragon's Teeth where is grows on shingle adjoining the salt-marsh. It has a black thorax, chestnut-wing cases, and six long legs. It is also recorded from the Portland and Weymouth end of the shingle but is otherwise unknown elsewhere in Britain.

There was no record of any specimen being found between 1926 and 1989 when a group of ten coleopterists were delighted to find more than a hundred specimens. Howard Mendel spotted the first, crawling on a thrift flower: 'I was overjoyed to see it there. We found it in far greater numbers than ever we dreamed. No one knows its life history. The larvae seem to live in the soil beneath the plant.'

Dorset's main little tern colonies are at either end of the Chesil Beach. Here at Abbotsbury, as at Ferrybridge, they nest amongst the pebbles and the area is managed as a local nature reserve. The birds and their eggs have full legal protection. Terns are conspicuous and noisy in flight and can be seen fishing in the shallow waters of The Fleet. Their nests, however, are well camouflaged, and a search for them is likely to end with a crushing sound beneath your feet. As they are now one of Britain's rarest breeding seabirds, and there are only a hundred pairs on the Chesil, you must observe the access restrictions.

This is the most westward colony of the little tern along the South Coast, the next to the east being at Beaulieu, in Hampshire. On 22 May 1985 the Chesil Beach and Fleet were designated by the Government as a 'Special Protection Area' under the European Community Bird Directive of 1979.

The onward mass of the Chesil Beach forms a great ridge of 100 million tonnes of shingle that grows in height and content-size all the way. It would appear to be globally unique in that despite exploration and satellite photography no one has found a beach quite like it. This wonder of the geological world is the classic example of a tombolo; a spit joined to land at both ends.

Denys Brunsden and Andrew Gourie observe in their guide to Dorset for the Geographical Association: 'It is remarkable for its size, its regular crest-line, its beautifully even curve, its lack of lateral ridges, its oft-quoted grading of pebble sizes. As a result, it is the most written about of all landforms in Britain.'

'Chesil' was the Old English word for pebble. The gravel at the West Bay end (and formerly from Golden Cap when the beach was continuous) is the sort you find in fish-tanks. By the time the beach reaches Portland it is composed of oval pebbles the size of saucers (called 'cobbles'). This phenomenon of the graduation of material into size by the action of water is called alutriation and can be replicated in a laboratory. From the flat start at Golden Cap and West Bay, the beach rises in stature as it goes, to 23 feet in height at Abbotsbury and 40 feet at Portland.

One theory is that it came into existence at a time of low sea levels caused by an Ice Age – the Devensian glacial which 'locked' water into glaciers – and was then a couple of miles into the Channel. It seems that the island of Portland must be the clue to its survival, acting as a huge groyne.

The materials were from a raised breach at Portland and the gravels of an extinct river that ran along The Fleet, available to wave-action after the sea had broken through and captured the valley. The action of the sea proceeded to grade the materials into a sequence of general eastwards growth, with the result that local fishermen landing in fog know their location to the nearest kilometre. The beach mainly comprises flint and chert with quartzites, a little local limestone, and odd stones from deposits as far west as Cornwall. These last stones could only have been acquired when the beach was further out to sea.

Towards Portland the crest-line of the beach can sometimes be moulded by a storm into ridges and gullies but these are temporary features. Seepage, washing out pebbles from the base, and the rolling of shingle from the crest, is causing the beach to continue its slow advance towards the mainland – lessening the width of The Fleet – at the rate of a metre per century.

Scientific evidence shows that the Chesil Beach is a finite resource; it is not being replenished by some shingle-making process out in the sea. Exploitation of the Chesil Beach at the 1970s rates of 27,000 tonnes a year would have seen it all removed in some 3000 years and start to cause coastal flooding nearer our time.

This is not a human environment. In the age of sail countless ships were driven by the south-westerlies, unbroken from the Atlantic, into the angle of the bank and Portland's groyne-like extension, which became known as Deadman's Bay. Before the use of rocket-fired lines there was no escape from the swirling pebbles. Even on a normal day there is an undertow that exhausts swimmers. Above the water, climbing up and down is almost painfully difficult.

Some masochists, like Roland Gant, have walked the 14 kilometres along the beach from Abbotsbury, to prove that Portland is not quite an island. If you want to do likewise allow a full 8-hour walking day. It is going to be too wild for comfort if strong south-westerly winds are forecast for Portland and bitterly slow against a cold easterly in winter. Do wrap up. If Storm Force 11 verges on Hurricane Force 12, and coincides with a particularly high tide, waves will surge over the top of the bank. That's an exceedingly rare event – but potentially deadly – so listen to the shipping forecast on Radio 4 before setting off.

Also respect the rights of the little tern! It is listed in schedule one of the Wildlife and Countryside Act 1981 which makes it an offence 'if any person intentionally disturbs' it 'while it is building a nest or is in or near a nest containing eggs or young'. Strangways Estates, agent E. W. S. Green told me: 'I would like to take the opportunity of pointing out that the Chesil Beach is closed during the nesting season – 1 May to 31 August. Both Strangways Estates and the Crown Commissioners, the owners of the Bank, welcome visitors outside the nesting season but would be grateful for your assistance in publicising the controls exercised in this important sea-bird nesting area.'

Gold coins are still occasionally washed up on the Chesil Beach but not in the quantity recorded by the *Dorset County Chronicle* of 18 December 1828: 'Many of the Portland islanders, as well as others, will be enabled to enjoy the Christmas holidays most merrily, from the effects of the late high tide and heavy gales of wind, which have been the means of throwing up on the beach bars of gold and silver. Guineas, crowns and dollars are picked up in abundance, which have been buried in the sea for many years from the various shipwrecks; the old adage "It is a bad wind that blows no one good" is thus amply verified.'

Many coins came from the Dutch ship *Hope*, returning up-Channel to her home port of Amsterdam, having been trading – or engaging in piracy – in the West Indies. The 350-ton, 30-gun treasure ship was wrecked on the Chesil Beach in 'tempestuous weather' on the night of 16 January 1749. The mast snapped and crashed on the beach, enabling the captain, Boii Cornelizs, and his 73 hands to clamber to safety on the pebbles.

'Ship ashore' was the cry that spread at day-break through Portland, Weymouth and the villages. Her cargo, mostly in gold, was worth £50,000 – a fortune in the then value of money – and well over half of it was plundered by 'a vast concourse' who pillaged the vessel 'as soon as the reflux of the sea had made the ship accessible'. They roughly pushed the crew aside and disregarded their faltering foreign accents, as the Dutch protested: 'No wreck. The goods ours. Bring it to we and we will pay for it.'

By this they meant salvage money, but the hostile crowd grew to an estimated 4000 people, who held the Chesil Beach for several days. They were organised by Augustin Elliott, a Portland labourer, who 'was the muster-master, the treasurer, and divider of the prey among his plundering regiment'.

They were eventually brought to a halt by three Justices of the Peace and an armed party which went on to carry out house-to-house searches and recover £25,000 for agents of the ship's owners. Elliott was put on trial at Dorchester on 15 July 1749 but acquitted by a sympathetic jury after a six-hour hearing.

One of the most remarkable Chesil Beach phenomena took place in 1841 when a groundswell 'laid bare for miles' the clay beneath the pebbles. Beachcombing, recovering the losses of ancient wrecks, thrived. People found antique rings, seals, silver, gold ingots and coins. Roman coins were 'most numerous' – especially the third-bronze from the fourth-century reign of Emperor Constantine – after a strong north-westerly wind had swept the shingle from the clay. The stones were not pushed back until the next south-westerlies.

In 1853 it was estimated that more than 4 million tons of shingle were swept into the sea during storms. Such transformations will happen again. The Chesil Beach remains one of the most exciting and dynamic geological features in the living landscape.

What colour is the Chesil Beach if all the pebbles are washed away? Blue is the answer, or bluish-grey to be precise, of Fuller's earth clay. Not that anyone in the twentieth century was able to vouch for this, from personal experience, but in Victorian times it was a known fact.

32 ABBOTSBURY SWANNERY

The monks of Abbotsbury established the Swannery beside The Fleet between Bum Point and Shipmoor Point (SY 576 840) before 1393. One of their square ponds still exists. Enticing and farming the swans provided them with a dependable source of feast-day meat. Abbotsbury Swannery came into the ownership of the Fox-Strangways family, later the Earls of Ilchester, in 1543, after Henry VIII had abolished the religious houses. The duck decoy at the Swannery was dug by its new owners in 1655.

Above – *Abbotsbury Swannery: beside The Fleet, opposite the Chesil Beach.* Above right – *Tranquil scene: typical of the western Fleet.*

The herd of mute swans tends to disperse to the other end of The Fleet in winter but returns to Abbotsbury for the spring. The pairs, which mate for life, then battle for the best nest sites – which can include sections of paths. Tourists are not admitted until the eggs are laid. There are currently an average of 100 pairs of which all but ten usually nest in the colony; the rest choose the overspill area on the Chesil Beach. Until 1935 there were in excess of 250 pairs in summer but a major slump occurred when their favourite food – eel grass – failed here and almost everywhere. Numbers subsequently recovered to 800 birds by the 1960s. Numbers in winter, then and now, always rise with an influx of visitors from points north and east, from the Severn to Siberia.

The 'royal birds' were said to be over-protected and took the blame for driving other birds from our rivers. Since then, however, it has been a steady decline, blamed nationally on lead poisoning caused by the swallowing of discarded fishing weights, which has afflicted a high proportion of river swans.

There have been problems at Abbotsbury as well, where the death of the legendary swanherd Fred Lexster 1982 coincided with the foul repercussions of the agricultural revolution, as his successors struggled against a cocktail of slurry effluent and farm chemicals. Over-nutrification, from the inflow of streams and the general leeching of nitrates and potassium from the land, resulted in an immense raft of blanket weed which smothered 5 kilometres of the West Fleet. Useless to birds, fish and wildlife generally, it is a reminder of the fragility of the coastal ecosystem.

33 THE FLEET

The shores of the brackish Fleet lagoon are worked by several hundred dunlin and oystercatchers but the coastal footpath diverts inland from the West Fleet and the only direct access is from the Elm Tree Inn at Langton Herring (SY 614 823). The shallow salt-waters cover 1250 acres and extend for 13 kilometres, separating the parishes of Abbotsbury, Langton Herring, Fleet and Chickerell from their seaward extremities on the offshore sweep of the Chesil Beach. The shore also hosts ringed plovers, grey plovers and lapwing. Common and little tern breed among the pebbles on the far side.

It's in winter, however, when the waters come alive. Fifty pairs of mute swan breed in summer but by midwinter there can be up to a thousand swans on the water. Wildfowl also flock south. Some 4000 widgeon comprise the third largest assembly of these birds in the West Country. There will also be a further thousand of mixed duck – spread between eider, goldeneye, mallard, pintail, pochard, shelduck, teal, tufted duck, and red-breasted merganser. A couple of hundred brent geese provide heavier company and prefer the pastures of neighbouring farms to the bleak shore between Abbotsbury and the Small Mouth opening into Portland Harbour.

34 LANGTON OYSTER BEDS

The low cliffs beside The Fleet at Langton Hive Point, north of the Langton Herring anchorage (SY 606 814) are composed almost entirely of grey layers of compressed oyster shells, preserved in the Fuller's earth clays. These are the species *Liostrea herbridica* – formerly mistaken for *Ostrea acuminata* – and the bed fits into the Jurassic sequence at the foot of the Fuller's earth clays. They are 200 million years old.

35 DAMBUSTER BOMBS

To a coast which saw a high attrition rate on both sides during the Battle of Britain in 1940, a solitary Wellington bomber returned in the winter of 1942-43, passing up and down off Langton Hive Point (SY 606 814) on the wartime Chesil Beach Bombing Range. It features in the archive clip towards the beginning of the famous film based on the Dambusters exploit.

The first prototypes of Barnes Wallis's revolutionary bouncing bomb were tested along The Fleet. Wooden versions evolved into concrete-filled steel spheres. Six of these half-size dummies were dropped and one or two remained beside the shore in post-war use as boat moorings. Operation Chastise, the epic raid which breached Mohne and Eder dams in the Ruhr was carried out by Lancaster bombers of 617 Squadron on the night of 16 May 1943, winning a Victoria Cross for Squadron Leader Guy Gibson.

In 1963, A. D. Grant of Vickers-Armstrongs (Aircraft) Limited at Weybridge, who was involved in the development of dambusting weapons, confirmed from a photograph that one of the Langton moorings was 'the remains of one of the original experimental spheres dropped behind the Chesil Bank from the Wellington allocated to Dr Wallis for these trials, to demonstrate the validity of his proposals for smashing the dams. These original spheres were made of relatively thin steel pressings welded together and stiffened with diaphragms. The earliest trials were carried out with the spheres empty so they floated and were readily recovered, but the impact on the water dented them so severely that a number were filled with concrete and served to demonstrate that non-floaters "ran" almost as far. The one in the photograph was dropped on March 8 or 9, 1943.'

36 HERBURY

The flat peninsula at Herbury (SY 613 809), on The Fleet lagoon between Langton Herring anchorage and Moonfleet Hotel is now famous for nothing, and is a place-name that has receded into ordinary decent obscurity. This were very different on 25 August 1982 when it was announced by the Central Electricity Generating Board that it was no longer under consideration as the site for a nuclear power station. This was to have been a reactor of the pressurised water type.

The Board announced that 'studies have shown that a single station development might be reasonably well shielded from view but that a double development would be more prominent' (bright lads, these power people). 'However, the site itself and the surroundings are of intrinsic natural beauty and ecological value which strongly weigh against its selection for development.'

That should have been obvious from the beginning. Anyway, the Board 'does not intend to proceed further with Herbury', which cynics might think was never really in the frame, serving as a diversion to draw attention from more likely candidates.

37 MOONFLEET HOTEL

Fleet Lane ends beside The Fleet lagoon where Moonfleet Hotel has put fiction into fact (SY 617 806). The former Fleet House, built by Maximilian Mohun in 1602, passed from the family that gave its name to Hammoon, into the hands of the Gould family in 1774 who rebuilt it in characteristic eighteenth century style.

That it is now Moonfleet is a mark of the impact made by the classical smuggling story of John Meade Falkner (1858-1932) which was based upon Mohun family traditions and the fact that smuggling was the main trade hereabouts. It is all a rattling good yarn, revived by BBC television under the title *Smugglers' Bay*.

Moonfleet Hotel has not lost its grip on these literary associations. In 1970, Bruce Hemingway converted the extensive cellars beneath the hotel into a dive-bar called Blackbeard's Vaults and the atmosphere was helped by a large stone trough, iron water pump, boat, kegs, smuggling notices, lantern, church-pew seating and a coffin. Above, the main lounge became the Mohun Arms, with a Why Not? Bar as an allusion to the family's armorial bearings which are shaped like a letter 'Y'.

38 FLEET CHAPEL

A terrace of cottages and the chancel of the old Fleet Church (SY 636 801) are all that survived when the sea swept over the Chesil Beach, and was funnelled into Butterstreet Cove, during a hurricane in 1824. Other buildings, below the churchyard, were completely washed away. There was a young eye-witness to the dramatic events that had his pals running for their lives at 08.00 hours on 23 November 1824:

'Most so soon as 'twas light a lot of us boys was out where we be a-standing, for to look at the seas what was coming over the ridge. Then after we'd been a-looking a goodish bit a thing happened differ'nt altogether. 'Twern't a sea – not a bit of it – twer the great sea hisself rose up level like, and come on right over ridge and all, like nothing in this world. We runned like made' till we was nigh up in Chickerell. When we comed back, where was the church? All but thic firm little chancel. All sucked away by that terrible rise of the sea. Went up to that there linchet, he did.'

Chancel story: the rest of old Fleet church was washed away in 1824.

The ruins of the nave were demolished in 1827 and the mediaeval chancel, with an original gable-cross, was rebuilt as a chapel. It contains attractive brasses to members of the Mohun family whose vault is beneath the floor. A legend of a secret passage between the church and a house was developed by John Meade Falkner into the classic Victorian smuggling adventure story, *Moonfleet*. It was given a degree of substance in 1925 when a strange structure was found two feet under the ground: 'The tunnel had solid walls, cemented on the inside, about five feet high and two feet wide, and was traceable across the churchyard.'

Fishing was often only a pretext for being near this coast and the coastal economy owed much to smuggling and the plunder of shipwrecks. On 22 December 1756, the vicar of Fleet, Rev. Thomas Francklyn, preached a sermon that reminded his parish-

Fleet hamlet: an unspoilt backwater.

ioners of the Acts of Parliament relating to ships that are stranded on the coast and in particular the penalties for the plunder of merchant goods: 'This has long been looked upon as a thing right and lawful to be done by them who received it from their fore-fathers, and practised it be-times. And, indeed, nothing can reconcile an act so shocking to any one's reason and conscience, but the frequency of committing.'

39 THE NARROWS

The Narrows of The Fleet are offshore from the military compounds at the end of Camp Road, Chickerell (SY 652 772). A rifle-range is on the low promontory at Tidmoor Point. The Bridging Hard of the Royal Engineers is beside the site of an engineering scheme in 1630 that was intended to drain the shallow salt-water lagoon. A wall was built, with sluices, by a consortium led by Sir George Horsey.

The land reclamation project failed because of the 'cans' under the Chesil Beach. These are holes through which the sea seems to flow into The Fleet. There is also leakage through the pebbles during gales. The remains of the wall have yet to be found. It was assumed by Professor Ronald Good to have been built across the Small Mouth estuary, but Dr Eric Bird pointed out that the currents at that point would have been too strong, and produced other evidence in favour of the Chickerell coast.

40 WYKE CASTLE and THE BOUND STONE

Wyke Castle at Wyke Regis is a make-believe Martello tower, mock-Gothic in Portland stone, beside Pirates Lane which leads to the coast path at Pirates Cove (SY 661 774). The track along the shore heads south-east, to three wartime pillboxes set as machine-gun nests in the scrub overlooking the offshore cages of Abbotsbury Oyster Farm.

Pirates Cove: the widest point up The Fleet at Wyke Regis.

Out on the Chesil Beach, two kilometres north-west of Ferrybridge Inn, the Bound Stone (SY 644 776) marks the boundary between the parishes of Chickerell and Portland. South-eastwards from it the beach is registered common land with a right of public access. Portlanders jealously guarded their rights and visited the stone annually on Ascension Day, or Holy Thursday as it was known. The present stone was delivered by air, being lowered from a Wessex helicopter of 516 Royal Naval Air Squadron, in 1974.

Inland, in Wyke Regis churchyard, lies William Lewis who has a headstone with a graphic carving depicting the interception of his smuggling vessel by a Customs service Revenue schooner, the *Pigmy*. The epitaph tells the rest:

Wyke Castle: an imitation Martello tower.

Coastguard lookout: in Westhill Road at Wyke Regis.

Sacred to the Memory
of William Lewis
who was killed by a shot from
the Pigmy Schooner 21st of
April 1822. Aged 22 years.

Of life bereft (by fell design),
I mingle with my fellow clay:
On God's protection I recline,
To save me on the Judgement Day.

There shall each blood-stain'd
soul appear. Repent all, ere it
be too late. Or else a dreadful
doom you'll hear; For God will
sure avenge my fate.

This stone is Erected by his
Wife as the last small respect to
an Affectionate Husband.

41 THE FERRYBRIDGE and SMALL MOUTH

With Abbotsbury Oyster Farm on one side and the former Whitehead Torpedo Works on the other, the Ferrybridge Inn (SY 667 763) takes its name from the now bridged boat crossing of the Small Mouth to Portland. Everything has changed on this Wyke Regis side of the entrance to The Fleet. Firstly, the red-brick hostelry used to be the Royal Victoria Hotel. Secondly, opposite, the torpedo factory which used to cover more than 7 acres with 200,000 square feet of buildings has become a housing estate. Thirdly, beside Portland Harbour, the viaduct that carried the island's branch railway was demolished in 1971.

Before the building of the first Ferry Bridge, in timber in 1839, there was a chain ferry operating here, powered by a horse plodding around a capstan. The cable was in a circuit, through the water and attached to the boat, with the return length via a pulley and suspended in mid-air. 'The passage boat', it was called, and Wyke people continue to refer to the Small Mouth area as being 'down Passage'.

An iron bridge was built in 1896, and replaced in 1985, due to corrosion and sinkage. On the other side, hidden under pebbles between the tide lines, lives the nation's only

Gunner's view: from an anti-invasion pillbox, across Small Mouth oyster beds to Portland.

known colony of the Mediterranean scaly cricket, *Mogoplistes squamiger*, which was confirmed as a British species in 1955 after Bernard C. Pickard found five adult specimens at the high-tide mark.

42 CHESIL COVE and ALLELUIA BAY

The primary building of Chesil Cove at Chiswell is the Cove House Inn (SY 683 734) which lies at the western foot of the heights described by Thomas Hardy as 'the Gibraltar of Wessex'. Modern sea defences, in wave-shaped concrete, defend Chiswell Square and nearby Maidenwell from repetition of the disastrous floods of 23 November 1824, 13 December 1942 and 13 February 1979. The first two left buildings in ruins, at Chiswell and Big Ope, and the third spilled over the top of the beach to flood Victoria Square to a depth of five feet.

Such freak waves have been blamed on tsunamis, caused by earthquakes on the mid-Atlantic tectonic divide, but further investigation of the 1979 flood showed its cause was a deep but dying depression 3200 kilometres to the south-west. Its outward wave crests were abnormally far apart and their arrival in Chesil Cove coincided with high tide and low pressure; the sea level was already a metre higher than that predicted.

Above left – *Chesil Cove: the wide sweep of the Chesil Beach at Chiswell.* Above – *Cove House: holding the front-line against the sea.*

Portland Heights: looking across to the mainland, along the Chesil Beach and the Fleet.

Verne Yeates: the closer view down to Fortuneswell and Chiswell.

Long waves came from across a full sea to hit the shingle bank frontally at 90 degrees, sweeping two metres of water across the top of the bank, and maintaining the wave form on its initial descent down the pebbles into streets and homes.

Public access southwards is courtesy of Hiram Otter who became a stalwart of Portland's new Salvation Army Corps and in 1885 proceeded to create Portland footpath No. 5 which snakes up from Chesil Cove, beneath West Weares, to the headland at Tar Rocks and Clay Ope beyond it (SY 681 724). He used his 'large and sinewy arms, with muscles of strong iron bands' to hand-jack immense boulders out of the way. Then he etched them with biblical inscriptions and the first lines of some of the Salvationists' powerful hymns. 'Alleluia!' he would cry when each of these text was completed.

Alleluia Bay: the end of Chesil Beach, towards Tar Rocks.

Alleluia Bay became the local name for the indented coast between Chesil Cove and Tar Rocks (SY 682 727). Silverwell, on the undercliff west of Priory Corner (SY 682 739), was renamed Jacob's Well.

43 TOUT QUARRY SCULPTURE PARK

Portland Sculpture Trust took on the old Tout Quarry (SY 683 723) in 1983. Worked continuously, from 1755 till 1905, the bramble-covered lunar landscape behind Priory Corner and West Weares cliff is being preserved as it was abandoned. Boulders and

Independent Quarry: with blocks of Portland stone awaiting transport.

Above – *Portland ammonite: a fresh specimen beside quarry tools.* Above right – *Lano's Bridge: Victorian arch, in carved stone without any cement.*

rock-faces have become the broad canvas for outdoor art on the grand scale. Some pieces are subtle but others are larger than life. Heads, animals and symbols abound.

It is as if a tribe of aboriginal cave artists has survived on the island who crawl out from under their stones in some crepuscular reincarnation to make magic marks before going to ground at dawn. Such images make one look at a quarry in a different way. Others echo architectural landmarks carved out of the quarry itself.

Quarrymen also have their memorials in the form of immense dry-stone walls and even a tramway bridge built without any mortar or cement. It carries a keystone for quarry-master 'J. C. LANO, 1854' and has almost unique winged voussoirs on either side to tie the ashlar facing stones into the random rubble behind. The quarry is on a thirty-year lease to Portland Town Council, from Hanson plc, who operate as Bath and Portland Stone.

Quarry manager Mark Godden of Albion Stone Quarries showed me fossils that had been newly found on the other side of Easton Drill Hall in Independent Quarry. These include the 3-metre diameter fossil tree-stump of a cycad fern, still with the remains of actual wood in the root ball, dating from the time before the gradual drift of plate tectonics had brought Britain into cooler climes. Our Jurassic position on the planet had a climate that is now found in the Middle East. The fossil trunk of a true tree species, a conifer from the Vicotrian convict quarries, stands beside Portland Heights Hotel.

Another incredibly rare find is a fusion of broken stalactites and calcite from the base of a former cave. 'It suffered catastrophic damage,' Mark said, 'which must have happened during the last Ice Age, when freezing and melting caused the stalactites to shear and fall to the floor, where the calcite has cemented them into a heap. I've never seen anything quite like it before.'

Rock art: in Tout Quarry Sculpture Park.

44 BLACKNOR FORT

The Victorian emplacement of Blacknor Fort, midway along Portland's western cliffs (SY 679 717) was re-equipped with four 9.2-inch guns in the First World War. Nearby, beside the coast path, two saucer-shaped pads of concrete mark the site of experiments with anti-aircraft rockets between 1937 and 1939. Fitted with 3-inch tubular charges, produced by the Royal Naval Cordite Factory, Holton Heath, they were tested by Explosives Research Department of the Royal Arsenal, Woolwich.

Beside the fort, on the 275-feet high grassland known as The Castles, Flying Officer James Murray Strickland of 213 Squadron from RAF Exeter had a notable triumph during the Battle of Britain. A German Junkers Ju.88 bomber, crippled in combat by the Hurricane, made a successful landing on the clifftop.

The gunners of Blacknor witnessed the so called Slapton Sands Massacre, of more than 600 American soldiers and seamen, on the night of 27 April 1944. They were ordered not to engage the German E-boats that had perpetrated the sinkings of the tank landing ships. because of the number of men who were swimming and drowning in Lyme Bay.

Blacknor Fort: view north, into Bower's Quarry and over Clay Ope.

45 ADMIRALTY UNDERWATER WEAPONS ESTABLISHMENT

The complex built across Barrow Hill, Southwell (SY 680 700) between 1949 and 1952 became infamous for Britain's most notorious Cold War espionage case. 'The stocky 39-year-old, whose true identity may never be known, faced Lord Parker, the Lord Chief Justice, with a smile on his face, a flush on his cheeks, and the fading words of his counsel in his ears: "At least it can be said of this man that he was not a traitor to his own country." But at the tone of Lord Parker's voice the smile vanished and he paled. A gasp broke the silence of the packed court at the sentence, twenty-five years – the longest passed there in memory.'

The report is from the front-page of the Daily Express and the date was 22 March 1961. The setting was the Old Bailey as members of the Portland spy-ring were sent down. Their 'control' at the Admiralty Underwater Weapons Establishment had been Gordon Lonsdale who was indeed no traitor to his country – being Russian. 'Lonsdale' was Colonel Conon Trimofovich Molody of the KGB. He did not stay in prison long enough to break any record, being swapped in Berlin on 21 April 1964, for Greville Wynne.

That one, we were told at the time, was an innocent British exhibition salesman, but he later turned into a self-confessed spy who had worked his Soviet contact – since shot – to good account during the Cuban missile crisis.

Western cliffs: above Ocean Rock, southwards to the Underwater Weapons Establishment.

46 PULPIT ROCK and PORTLAND BILL

The famous feature of Portland Bill, its Pulpit Rock (SY 676 683) was created about 1875 when quarrymen working the adjoining Beacon Quarry left a chunk of cliff standing proud from the ledges of their working floor. It is the southern-most tip of both Dorset and the World Heritage Site. On the other side of the quarry, beside and inside military chain-link fencing, is a 200,000-year-old geological rarity. Known as Portland Raised Beach it came into being during a warm inter-glacial period of the Pleistocene ice ages.

It is now a platform, 10 metres above the highest tides, comprising pebbles, stones, gravel, shells and sand fused into a calcareous mass by constant weathering. This under-layer is about 1½ metres thick and covered by a wind-deposited stratum of orange sandy silt, about 2 metres in depth. Above this comes a deep brown solifluction deposit, a couple of feet thick, which was formed during the last major glacial period, the Devensian.

Raised beach: from a warm Pleistocene interlude, protected by military fencing.

Portland Bill as a placename has its roots in 'The Beel' of early maps, apparently deriving from the beak shape of the projecting headland – as in a bird's bill – that has almost

Above – *Pulpit Rock: the stone cliffs to the south, from above Powell's Tar.* Above right – *Southern tip: with* Waverley *paddle-steamer rounding the Bill into Lyme Bay.*

entirely eclipsed its other local name. From 1588 onwards, when it had a crucial bonfire in the Armada invasion-warning network, it was known as The Beacon.

Here the beacon chain turned the corner, from Thorncombe Beacon and Abbotsbury, and signalled its warning to St Alan's Head in the Purbeck quarrylands. From there, via Beacon Hill at Lytchett Minster and St Catherine's Hill above Christchurch, the pivotal point in the network was on the Isle of Wight. There the watchers could pass the alert directly inland, to Southampton, Winchester and London, as well as to Portsmouth and the Sussex coast.

Sir John Clayton was awarded a patent to erect a lighthouse on 'the Bill of Portland' in 1699 and to show two lights from this tower. He failed to proceed with this consent, and the first lighthouses – a pair – would be built in 1716. Trinity House had obtained a patent in May 1716 and granted a lease to William Barrett and Francis Browne for £100. Charles Langridge stoked the coals to illuminate their glazed lanterns for the first time on 29 September 1716.

Barrett and Browne were to build and maintain 'one or more convenient lighthouses with good and visible lights to be kept continually there in the night season, so as ships might the better come to their ports without peril'. The Customs Office, London, was instructed to collect dues from all ships passing the light, at a rate of a halfpenny per ton levied on English ships, and a penny a ton from foreign vessels.

The Lower Light (SY 681 690) was reconstructed in 1789 and was 19 metres high. Both it and the Upper Light (SY 677 693) were demolished and rebuilt in 1869. They survive, with the Upper Light having been the home of contraception pioneer Dr Marie Stopes, and the Lower Light is now the Bird Observatory. The Shambles sandbank, offshore, was marked by a lightship on 1 May 1859.

The current Lighthouse (SY 678 684) was constructed between 1903 and 1905. The circular stone tower was built by Wakeham Brothers of Plymouth. It has 153 steps and is 136 feet high. Three tons of lens float at the top of a liquid metal base of half a ton of mercury. Its night-time white flashes are in fact a group of four lights, giving a beam every 20 seconds. This equals 3,370,000 candles and is visible in clear weather for 28 kilometres. The lights are set at 43 metres above the high water mark. An additional red light illuminates the water over the Shambles sandbank.

Navigation beacon: placed on Portland Bill by Trinity House.

Close to ground level, seaward of the tower, the fog horn is activated as visibility falls to less than two miles and gives a blast of three and a half seconds at half minute intervals.

Nearby, on the edge of the cliff, an 1844-dated stone pyramid is a navigation beacon. Its 'TH' lettering stands for Trinity House rather than four-year-old Thomas Hardy (as I have to reply to readers at least every other year) though Portland Bill makes frequent appearances in his work. In his remarkable 1899 poem *The Souls of the Slain* the spirits of soldiers killed in the South African War fly homeward over Portland Bill like migratory moths. He also likened Portland Bill to the outstretched beak of a bird. 'The wild, herbless, weather-worn promontory' provides the setting in *The Trumpet Major* for Anne Garland to watch H.M.S. *Victory* sailing for Plymouth and Cape Trafalgar with Bob Loveday on board.

Portland Bird Observatory, in the former Lower Lighthouse, opened to ornithologists in 1961 and soon established a reputation as the one place in southern England where melodious and icterine warblers make dependable annual appearances. Some 2000 migrant birds make their landfall into waiting mist-nets. Warblers are a speciality, including the aquatic warbler, Bonelli's warbler, sub-Alpine warbler and yellow-browed warbler. Occasionally there is the excitement of American visitors that are freak windfalls from the jet stream.

47 PORTLAND RACE and THE SHAMBLES

Offshore turbulence, where spring tides exceed 7 knots, is visible from Portland Bill (SY 677 683). The best advice for navigating around the Bill is to pass outside the Race on a course three miles south of the red-banded Lighthouse and Trinity House beacon in calm weather. In a gale, especially during spring tides when the wind is

The Lighthouse: 136 feet high, built in 1905.

Far left – *Candle power: the main lamp equals 3,750,000, visible for 28 miles in clear weather.* Left – *Bill buildings: looking east towards the Shambles.*

against the flow, it is advisable to give Portland a miss by 8 kilometres. Part of the problem is that the confused and dangerous waters then spread across the entire area around the Bill including the Shambles sandbank which lies a mile to the south-east.

An engagement with the Spanish Armada took place off Portland Bill on 23 July 1588. It was a lack lustre affair which achieved nothing except for the Spanish who moved on to mid-Channel and a day's sailing time nearer their Dutch interim destination without the loss of any more ships. Indeed it might have turned out a positive victory for the enemy if the day's opportunities had been taken.

Don Hugo de Moncada wanted to take advantage of the calm conditions the previous night to move his oar-powered galleasses – light but powerfully gunned highly manoeuvrable craft that were a cross between a galley and a galleon – in an attack on the English flagship. The *Ark*, 800 tons, had been built by Sir Walter Raleigh and sold to Queen Elizabeth I. It now carried the flag of her Lieutenant-General and Commander-in-Chief of the Navy, the Lord High Admiral of England, fifty-two-year-old Charles Howard, Baron Howard of Effingham.

Moncada's intentions were blocked by his Commander-in-Chief, the Admiral of the Ocean thirty-eight-year-old Alonso Perez de Guzman, 7th Duke of Medina-Sidonia. Despite a complete lack of nautical experience he was in command of the 'Invincible Armada' that was undertaking this 'Enterprise of England'. His were the ethics of a nobleman, rooted in mediaeval chivalry, where like could fight only with like. It would only be honourable for Sidonia to engage Howard; Moncada was therefore refused permission to attack.

The initiative passed to the English. In an off-shore north-easterly breeze at 05.00 hours the rash but gallant Martin Frobisher, fifty-three-year-old veteran of the searches for the Canadian Northwest passage, took the *Triumph* and five other ships eastward through the tricky inshore waters between the Spanish fleet and the rocks of the Portland Bill peninsula. He judged the wind perfectly and slipped into the outer waters of Weymouth Bay, between Portland Bill and St Alban's Head. No one could fault Frobisher's seamanship but his strategy was questionable – he had chosen to box himself into a corner.

Howard hesitated about following. He was too cautious to risk placing the *Ark* between the enemy and the rocks and held back his cluster of vessels. The Armada's rearguard, led by de Leyva, Oquendo and Bertendona, closed in to attempt boardings as Sidonia himself swung towards the action. Howard also seemed to be closing for a fight as he led his line of England's biggest ships towards the *San Martin*. They came to within 100 to 120 metres. Purser Pedro Calderon's *Relacion* of the action is that the *San Martin* withstood considerable fire: 'The enemy shot at the Duke at least 500 cannon-balls, some of which struck the hull and others his rigging, carrying away his flagstaff and one of the stays of the mainmast.' Fifty were killed.

The damage, however, was not critical. Neither was that which the *San Martin* inflicted upon Howard's ships, even though Calderon says she 'fired over 80 shots from one side only, and inflicted great damage'. He realised, however, that the engagement was essentially a failure as the Spanish were constantly 'trying to come up with them' and failing to close in sufficiency on the English vessels. There was also a missing element of luck; the Spaniard's heavier 50-pound cannon-balls failed to smash the *Ark's* rigging.

Meanwhile Frobisher's division of the English fleet was potentially isolated. Sir Francis Drake was saw its quandary and was in no mood to take the Revenge inshore to join them. Frobisher, however, could not be under-estimated. He set about showing that the galleasses could not take on standard warships in a straight fight and he used his great galleon – the *Triumph* was just about the largest ship from either England or Spain – to smash his way out of trouble.

Instead of closing sufficiently to try and hole their hulls he used his massive fire-power to rake the rowing decks of the galleasses and immobilise both the oarsmen and their oars. Morcada had to revert to sails and thereby lost the whole manoeuvring advantage of the galleasses. None of the cornered English vessels would be lost and the Spaniards had taken a mauling in an attack which they were now forced to abandon.

By noon the wind had strengthened and backed to the south-west. It carried with it, fast up-Channel, 50 English vessels spearheaded by Drake in the *Revenge*. Howard realised that the initiative was now his and once again attacked the *San Martin*. Drake went for the rearguard commander, Juan Martinez de Recalde, his principal target of previous engagements, but as before Recalde could count on his other vessels for support. The Armada was able to return to its formations and use the south-west wind to take it on past St Alban's Head and towards the Isle of Wight.

A later Battle of Portland was hardly a 'famous victory', as has been claimed, but nearly a disaster for both the English and Dutch fleets as they fought off Portland Bill on 18 February 1653. Admiral Robert Blake (1599-1657) was lucky to escape with his life, and Maarten Harpertszoon Tromp (1597-1653) was fortunate to survive with the bulk of his ships.

Blake blundered by taking his red squadron alone to intercept Tromp's full fleet. The English flagship, the *Triumph*, was heavily engaged, with the loss of its captain, and Blake was severely wounded.

Not until the afternoon did Vice-Admiral Sir William Penn (1621-70) arrive with the blue and white squadrons of the English fleet to make an even battle. By next morning the ships were off St Catherine's Point, Isle of Wight, and Tromp escaped up-Channel. He had lost five warships sunk and four captured, and 40 merchant ships were also lost, but the main Dutch fleet survived to fight again. Tromp would be killed by the British, led by Monck, off Texel Island later in the year.

The waters off Portland saw three world 'firsts' in the history of naval aviation. Lieutenant Charles Rumney Samson (1883-1931) became the first pilot in the world to take off in an aeroplane from a moving ship. He took off in a Short Pusher amphibian biplane from the forecastle of the battleship H.M.S. *Hibernia* as she steamed at 10.5 knots off Portland during the Naval Review of May 1912. His reward that evening was an invitation to dine with King George V aboard the royal yacht *Victoria and Albert*.

Helicopter pilot Lieutenant Alan Bristow (born 1923) of 771 Royal Naval Air Squadron, brought his Fleet Air Arm Sikorski R4B Hoverfly down on to the makeshift

Channel view: Portland's indented eastern seaboard.

floorboard flight-deck of trials ship K253, the frigate H.M.S. *Helmsdale*, off Portland on 6 September 1946. It was the first helicopter landing on a naval escort-vessel at sea.

Chief test pilot Alfred William 'Bill' Bedford (born 1920) achieved the first vertical landing by a fixed wing aircraft on an aircraft-carrier when he brought his Hawker Siddeley P1127 Kestrel, prototype of the Harrier, down on H.M.S. *Ark Royal* as she sailed at 5-knots to the east of the Shambles on 8 February 1963.

48 BOAT-HAULS and CAVE HOLE

Derricks used to winch fishing boats in and out of the sea, from the top of sheer cliffs on the south-east side of the island, include Red Crane (SY 680 685) which is closest to Portland Bill. The other boat-hauls are beside Limekiln Cave (SY 689 696) and God Nore (SY 691 698). They are former quarry winches.

Cave Hole is the sea cave beneath the coast path a kilometre north-east of Portland Bill (SY 687 690). Blow holes stretch far into the rock. You can look down into it from the path, through the fissures, but without sensing its true proportions. The interior cavern is 15 metres square and 6.4 metres high.

Small craft have been driven into it by south-easterly gales. The largest was a 40-ton vessel from Cowes in 1780. Formerly the name of the cave was Keeve's and it figures in many of Portland's smuggling tales, with the legends being kept alive by an eerie boom from beneath the ground during heavy seas.

It is particularly dangerous and dramatic in an easterly gale when the sea snorts up through cracks in the path along a series of blow-holes. The ketch *Reliance* was wedged half inside it in a storm in 1949 and became a total loss.

Limekiln Cave is another massive sea cave between Portland Bill and Southwell (SY 689 696). Twelve metres inland is a sizeable blow-hole, capped with an iron grill.

49 CHEYNE WEARE

The 1.5 acre clifftop picnic area of Cheyne Weare is set on a dramatic slant with panoramic views from Portland's eastern quarrylands beside Southwell Road (SY 693 704). It is part of the Southwell landslip of 1665. The former spoil tip was cleaned up by ARC Southern and provided with stone benches facing seaward, looking over Weymouth Bay to St Alban's Head and the Isle of Wight.

The construction company presented the land to Portland Town Council in 1987 for a peppercorn rent of £1 a year. 'Cheyne Weare has been the best place for generations for the island's fishermen to spot shoals of mackerel,' quarry manager John Reay said at the hand-over ceremony.

50 CHURCH HOPE COVE and RUFUS CASTLE

The picturesque but stony east-facing bay tucked away beneath Rufus Castle, and the ruined mediaeval church of St Andrew, is reached by a dramatic flight of steps (SY 697 710). Rows of beach-huts are crammed on to anywhere resembling a flat space between the top of the beach of Church Hope Cove and the sheer cliffs.

It was named firstly for the old church and secondly for the 'ope' which was local dialect for 'an opening in the cliffs down to the water's edge', according to Dorset philologist William Barnes. 'Cove' sums up its other attribute; the small, rounded bay. 'Churchhope was its name as long ago as 1710.

Far left – *Church Ope: a rocky cove.* Left – *Commanding position: Bow and Arrow Castle upstages the beach-huts.*

The beach and rugged cliffs are registered common land. Rufus Castle is alternatively known as Bow and Arrow Castle and rises as a romantic ruin from its perch on a precipice (SY 697 712) with a squat, roofless tower in the floor-plan of a pentagon. This was built in the fifteenth century and has a nineteenth-century gateway and bridge.

It is said to have been built on the site of an earlier castle constructed in the time of William II, nicknamed King Rufus, who reigned from 1087 to 1100. This was captured by Robert, Earl of Gloucester, in 1142. The rebuilding was carried out by Richard, Duke of York, between 1432 and 1460.

51 PENNSYLVANIA CASTLE

A Gothic mock-fortification, Pennsylvania Castle is surrounded by the sycamores of Portland's only wood, on the clifftop above Church Ope Cove (SY 695 711). It was built in 1800, for John Penn (1760-1834), to designs by eminent architect James Wyatt (1746-1813). The double pun behind its name was that Penn's grandfather, William Penn (1644-1718), had founded Pennsylvania.

Portland's Penn was a writer, poet and dramatist who founded a 'matrimonial society' in 1817 to improve the domestic life of married persons. It became the Outlinian Society and continued to meet until 1825. Oddly, in the circumstances, Penn himself was unmarried.

He was a playwright, with *The Battle of Eddington or British Liberty* being performed at Windsor, The Haymarket, Covent Garden and Sadler's Wells. He also translated Virgil and wrote his own poems, which were published on the private press at his other seat, Stoke Poges Park in Buckinghamshire. There is a memorial to him in St George's Church, at Reforne, on Portland.

52 PORTLAND MUSEUM

The thatched Avice's Cottage, at the south end of the wide street in Wakeham (SY 696 713) was given by birth control pioneer Dr Marie Stopes to the island and, with the contemporary cottage adjoining, became Portland Museum in 1930. Its 1640 datestone links it with first owner Bartholomew Mitchell.

As well as being a rarity in its own right, as there are only a couple of thatched cottages on the island, Avice's Cottage has the distinction of having been used by author Thomas Hardy (1840-1928) to provide virtually the entire setting for his novel

The Well-Beloved, written as a magazine serial in 1892 and published as a book in 1897. Portland is the 'Isle of Slingers' – Chesil Beach pebbles having been used as slingstones by prehistoric man – and Avice's Cottage features as the home of would-be well-beloved Avice Caro. She dies and is followed by two other unattainable Avices. 'All men are pursuing a shadow,' Hardy said, when taken to task on his improbable plot.

53 THE GROVE PRISON

Now a Youth Offender Institution, the original Victorian Portland Prison in The Grove (SY 703 723) provided convict labour for the Admiralty Quarries, producing vast quantities of stone for the construction of the breakwaters that form Portland Harbour. The austere buildings standing on the plateau at 334 feet above East Weares and Folly Pier housed some of the best known prisoners of the age. Three very different characters became household names.

Convict prison: austere Victorian architecture now restrains a younger clientele.

John 'Babbacombe' Lee was twenty-two-years-old on 23 February 1885 when he experienced the longest forty-five minutes of his life. The noose was put around his neck three times, in Exeter Gaol, and the lever was pulled but the trapdoor jammed on each occasion. A warder jumped on and off as the hangman tried to free the pulleys. Sentence of death, for the murder of Mrs Keyse, a former lady-in-waiting to Queen Victoria, was then postponed and later commuted to life imprisonment, which was served on Portland until 1907.

He was then released as a living legend – 'the man they couldn't hang' – with media attention, songs, comic strips and even an early cinema film. The circumstantial evidence on which he had been convicted was twisted into ever more far-fetched fictions. Even King Edward VII, who as the Prince of Wales had been a frequent visitor to the house of Mrs Keyse, at Babbacombe near Torquay, was cited as the culprit.

Irish rebel Thomas J. Clarke – convicted under the name of Wilson – arrived at The Grove in 1884 to begin a life sentence for conspiring with the Fenian or Irish Revolutionary Brotherhood to dynamite public buildings in England. He was released under an amnesty in 1898 and went on to issue his own death warrant, on 23 April 1916, in the form of the first and only edition of *The Irish Republic*. This announced the Sinn Fein Easter uprising with Thomas J. Clarke topping the list of members of the 'Provisional Government'.

In 1892, Portland received convict V.460, fraudster and runaway Member of Parliament for Burnley, whose group of companies had collapsed. Britain's greatest economic criminal of the nineteenth century, he was extradited from Argentina, to stand trial at the Old Bailey. On arrival in Dorset for hard labour, Jabez Balfour wrote: 'There is no necessity to carve the words "Abandon hope, all ye who enter here" over the entrance to Portland Prison. The massive, cold grey walls say that for themselves.'

The prison population of 1600 included 700 quarrymen and 400 masons whose job was to supply the 'Free workmen' – navvies and artisans – working down on the breakwaters. Conditions were harsh, sparking a riot and break-out on 12 September 1858, and on 18 August 1869 a prisoner named Hatheridge was hanged at Dorchester for the murder of a warder.

54 NICODEMUS NOB

The prominent sea-mark on the cliff-edge beside the former Admiralty Quarries is Nicodemus Nob (SY 699 729), standing ten metres high, which was left a rough lozenge-shaped rock when the remaining stone was quarried away by Victorian convicts.

My guess is that it was cut as a boundary marker for 'the Common or Weir' (Portland cliffs being called Weares) and that it takes its name from Nicodemus Knowle. This name was in use in Victorian times for the cliff below The Grove. Another section was called Shepherd's Dinner.

55 HIGH ANGLE BATTERY

The main Victorian artillery defences for protecting the approaches to Portland Harbour are set out of sight from the sea, some distance inland from East Wears on the plateau south of Verne Citadel (SY 694 733). Fifteen huge rifled muzzle-loaded cannon were set into the ground, supplied from tunnels by a miniature railway, with steeply elevated trajectories pre-set to land shells on the course vessels would have to take to enter the ship channels into the harbour.

The battery was built in 1892 and emplaced with six 9-inch guns (range 8 kilometres), two 12.5-inch (range 8 kilometres), one 10-inch gun (range 5 kilometres), one 8-inch (range 4 kilometres), and five 7-inch (range 3 kilometres). All were designed to fire Palliser-type shells into the first generation of iron-clad battleships. Each had elaborate carriages and elevating gear which weighed upwards of 20 tons in combination with the gun barrels. They were sold for scrap but the barbettes, rails and underground bunkers survived, and were restored by a community project in 1984.

High Angle: defending the harbour approaches from deep in the island.

56 VERNE CITADEL now PORTLAND PRISON

The great Victorian fortress on the top of The Verne above Castletown and Fortuneswell (SY 692 737) was taken over by the Home Office Prison Service in 1948 and currently holds 520 men of medium security status. Verne Citadel, as it used to be known, was built between 1860 and 1872 on the site of an Iron Age hill-fort mentioned by seventeenth-century antiquary John Aubrey. The dry-moat on the landward side, 136 metres wide and 21 metres deep, was used as a rifle range.

Convict labour removed 1,500,000 tons of stone from this moat for the Outer Breakwater of Portland Harbour. It was the largest single source of stone. Designed by Captain Crossman of the Royal Engineers, the 50-acre fortress had nine fixed and ten mobile artillery pieces, with the former weighing 32 tons. Underground shell-proof barracks housed 1000 troops. The 1881-dated rear entrance, an afterthought, was used for manning the nearby High Angle Batttery.

Verne Citadel: now a prison, the island's main fortress is behind a huge dry moat.

Above and right – *Verne Citadel: now a prison, the island's main fortress is behind a huge dry moat.*

57 PORTLAND HARBOUR

'THESE ARE IMPERIAL WORKS AND WORTHY KINGS' boasts a great block of stone at the Castletown end of Portland Breakwater (SY 697 743). 'From this spot on the 25th of July 1849 His Royal Highness Prince Albert, consort of Queen Victoria, sunk the first stone of the breakwater. Upon the same spot, Albert Edward, Prince of Wales, on the 10th of August 1872 laid this last stone and declared the work complete.'

That statement was somewhat premature as an extensive second stage of breakwater building would follow between 1894 and 1903. A 'Harbour of Refuge' had been provided for the Home Fleet with 6½ square kilometres of deep water being enclosed behind massive walls of stone. It is bigger than anything created in the colonies and is indeed one of the peaks of British engineering achievement. It is the largest man-made harbour in the world.

The first two arms of the breakwater contain 5,750,000 tons of stone and took three decades of momentous effort to construct. The record for a single week's work saw 25,000 tons of stone being dumped below the waves. Railways and cages of scaffolding edged into the sea using the method devised by James Meadows Rendel (1799-1856) for the deep-water Millbay Pier at Plymouth. Pile-driving preceded the advancing structure and months of work were sometimes lost to stormy weather. Stones ranged from 6-ton boulders down to hand-sized pieces with the latter being just as important as the former because mixed sizes were essential to ensure even compacting. On Rendel's death the project was taken over by John Cooke (1816-92). Were we a nation that praises famous engineers we would talk of Rendel and Cooke in the same breath as Telford and Smeaton.

Finishing touches include two immense forts with Fort Head being more than 1½ kilometres out to sea and having the futuristic look of a flying-saucer. Its main anti-ship armament comprised seven 12.5-inch rifled muzzle-loaded cannon each weighing 38 tons and mounted on a carriage and platform weighing a further 12 tons. Other weapons were emplaced to fire towards Portland in case of an enemy landing on the island.

The main threat in the next century came from German U-boats. Anti-submarine nets blocked the North Ship Channel and East Ship Channel but the other entrance to Portland Harbour was closed completely. This was achieved on 4 November 1914, by scuttling a redundant iron-clad, the 14,000-ton battleship H.M.S. *Hood*.

In the Second World War, from July 1940, the proximity of the Luftwaffe on the Cherbourg peninsula minimised Portland's naval role. All that changed when Allied

Outer harbour: the arms of its breakwaters, seen from Verne Citadel.

offensive superiority led to the decision to launch a Second Front. Portland Harbour and Weymouth Harbour were allocated to V Corps of the United States Army – designated Force O for Omaha. On D-Day, 6 June 1944, they comprised a key part of the biggest armada in history and suffered more than 2000 dead in taking the bloodiest of the Normandy beaches. A concrete Phoenix caison, offshore from Castleton, was devised as a floating section of temporary Mulberry Harbour for towing across the English Channel, but never left Portland Harbour.

Below left – *Mulberry Harbour: section of wartime concrete that failed to reach Normandy, seen from Castletown.* Below – *Portland Castle: with the Boscawen Centre behind.*

58 PORTLAND CASTLE

Dorset's only intact castle, Portland Castle (SY 684 743) was built in 1540 by Henry VIII, with low, solid stone walls of massive thickness to withstand the new age of gunpowder. It was part of a master plan to protect the Channel coast from surprise attack, being at the western end of a string of such blockhouses, of which Hurst Castle, at the mouth of the Solent, was the strongest. Several played their part in conflicts for the rest of the millennium.

In the Civil War, Portland Castle was one of the first fortresses garrisoned for Parliament but it then changed hands and was one of the last pockets of Royalist resistance in the West until surrender at the end of the war, on 4 April 1646. The Governor of the Castle and Isle of Portland, Colonel Thomas Sidney Gollop, and his men were free to 'march away with all their horses, not surmounting the number 15, full arms, match alight, bullet in mouth, colours displayed, drums beating, and band and baggage to Oxford'.

Portland Castle is in the care of English Heritage and open to the public.

59 SANDSFOOT CASTLE

The partner to Portland Castle, on the opposite side of the former Weymouth road anchorage, Sandsfoot Castle at Southlands (SY 675 774) dates from 1541. It is now a ruin and has lost its gun-platform over the cliff in landslips. The last gun embrasure of the business end, an octagonal block-house, fell into the sea in the 1950s. Behind it, the remains of a rectangular building held the barracks and storeroom, on two floors with fireplaces, staircases and a basement. An integral gate-tower is incorporated in one corner.

Outside, about 100 feet from the walls, there are traces of a landward defensive earthwork. This was added in 1623, with a bank and outer ditch, at a time when Sandsfoot Castle was armed with ten heavy guns. It was held by the Royalists in 1644-45 but then abandoned. Until 1691 it was used as a store and has been derelict ever since.

Romantic ruin: Henry VIII's coast defences tottering on the edge.

Far left – *Gun platform: now lying across the beach.* Left – *Inside out: back view towards Weymouth suburbia.*

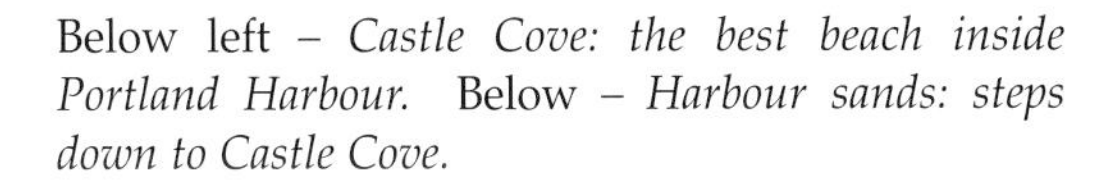

Below left – *Castle Cove: the best beach inside Portland Harbour.* Below – *Harbour sands: steps down to Castle Cove.*

60 PORTLAND HOUSE

The split-level Spanish hacienda-style art-deco villa on the south side of Belle Vue Road at Rodwell, Portland House (SY 680 779) was designed for the Bushby family in 1935, by architect Gerald Wellesley, later the 7th Duke of Wellington (1885-1972). There is a magnificent staircase descending from the upper to lower ground-floors with curved and bevelled treads and tiled risers. The Crittal-Hope windows are the forerunner of galvanised metal casements. Exterior paintwork has always been 'Delphinium Blue'.

Superb formal grounds, with sweeping lawns and a colonnade of palms, enhance the Mediterranean atmosphere and overlook Portland Harbour and its breakwaters. Underbarn Walk is at the bottom of the garden.

Portland House, including the undercliff and foreshore beside the Western Ledges, is owned by the National Trust. Six acres were donated by Miss Dorothy Esther Bushby in 1970 but the building and grounds are let and have no public access.

61 THE NOTHE FORT

Beside gardens laid out in the 1880s, the Nothe Fort on the promontory south of Weymouth Harbour (SY 687 788) had a prolonged role in coastal defence, from before 1585 until after the Second World War. Its semi-circular defences project eastwards into Weymouth Bay in a location originally chosen for the 'Jutty' or Jetty Fort that was also known as Queen Elizabeth's Fort. In 1641, being then just a mole of rocks, the jetty was called the Molehead.

Its other name was 'The North' (recorded in 1604 and 1649) which it shared with the 'White North' above Ringstead Bay. These names have become The Nothe and White Nothe respectively. Re-fortification of The Nothe, at the time of the Franco-Prussian War, was ordered by the Royal Commission on the Defence of the United Kingdom which was set up by Viscount Palmerston and reported in 1860.

By 1862 The Nothe was under construction and held ten 9-inch rifled muzzle-loaded guns a decade later. These were displaced by breech-loading guns in 1902. The Nothe had already been converted into an infantry barracks, in 1890, and held 200 men. Searchlights and Bofors 40-mm anti-aircraft guns, firing 120 rounds per minute, were installed in 1940. Steel and concrete emplacements for 6-inch anti-ship guns were erected above the Victorian brick and stone batteries in 1941. Nothe Fort was stood down in 1956 and is now the local military museum.

Clockwise, starting from left – *Nothe Fort: entrance beside municipal gardens.*
Victorian gunner: readiness at No. 11 battery.
Seaward corner: the immensity of Victorian war-works.
Outer curve: typical Palmerstonian fortification, hiding a central courtyard.

62 WEYMOUTH HARBOUR and ESPLANADE

The infamous fact about the Melcombe Regis side of Weymouth Harbour, in the vicinity of the present Custom House Quay (SY 681 788), was the port of entry for the Black Death into the British Isles. The Plague, the great pestilence of the Middle Ages, had made its landfall, according to the monk who compiled the chronicle at Grey Friars, King's Lynn, 'a little before the Feast of St John the Baptist' - that is, before 24 June, in 1348.

This is his record of the arrival of the disaster that, according to the more cautious estimates, wiped out a third of the population of Europe in the years 1347 to 1350: 'In this

Above – *Channel ferry:* Sarnia, *at Weymouth, was on the Channel Islands run.* Right – *Weymouth Harbour: where the Plague entered England.*

Above left – *Weymouth Lifeboat: self-righting tower of marine technology.* Above – *Sailors Return: appropriately named, watching over the Backwater.*

year 1348, in Melcombe in the county of Dorset, a little before the Feast of St John the Baptist, two ships, one of them from Bristol, came alongside. One of the sailors had brought with him from Gascony the seeds of the terrible pestilence and, through him, the men of that town of Melcombe were the first in England to be infected.'

Melcombe, which had yet to lose its name to Weymouth, was then one of the major ports in the land and had sent almost as many vessels to the Siege of Calais as had Bristol and London. The monk may well be right about the origin of the infected sailor but the statistical probability is that the infection had come from the Channel Islands as these, as now, had Weymouth Harbour as their lifeline with England.

Weymouth also features in Irish history. An order was signed in Whitehall on 30 November 1598 for Sir John Fortescue, the Chancellor of the Exchequer, and Lord Buckhurst, the Lord Treasurer, to reimburse the Mayor of Weymouth and Melcombe Regis the sum of £588-19s-10d for victuals and other necessities which the town provided for the troops waiting to embark for Ireland. It was signed by Robert Devereux, Earl of Essex; Charles Howard, Earl of Nottingham; Roger North; Thomas Sackville, Baron Buckhurst; William Knollys; Robert Cecil; Sir John Fortescue; William Waad; and John Whitgift, Archbishop of Canterbury. Fortescue appended a note: 'Mr Skynner make an order for this money.'

Golden jubilee: Weymouth's gaudy tribute to the King who made the seaside fashionable.

The *Dictionary of English History* sees little credit in the sixteenth century colonisation of Ireland: 'The policy of the government was not to subdue, but to destroy. Women and infants were regularly murdered. A well-planned famine removed the fugitives. Munster was a desert, fit at last for the civilisation of the Raleighs and Spensers. Half a million acres were bestowed on English adventurers.'

Weymouth's future as a fashionable seaside spa was established by George III (1738-1820) who reigned from 1760 and adopted the Dorset port. He is commemorated by a one-acre hill figure above Osmington in 1808 and an imposing statue at the southern end of the Esplanade in 1809. This was moulded in Coade stone by 'the Grateful Inhabitants of Weymouth' and painted in gaudy heraldic colours. Prince Charles considers it would have been better for the British Empire if the King had forgone a summer in Weymouth and pioneered the concept of an overseas state visit:

'King George III's cardinal error was that he failed in history – he failed to retain the American colonies and in the search to find a scapegoat for this national disaster, the King became the obvious target. Few laboured harder at being a good King than George the Third. He cared. The tragedy is that the American colonies never received a visit from him – if a royal tour had been a conceivable undertaking in the eighteenth century, the leaders of the colonies might have understood him better.'

Jane Austen found Georgian Weymouth enervating and described it as 'one of the idlest haunts in the kingdom'.

Hope Quay: graced by a visit from The Matthew *in 2001.*

Alexandra Gardens, named for Queen Alexandra, are on 'The Rings' at the south end of the Esplanade where fairs and circuses used to be pitched. The land was bought for the town by G. R. Stephenson in 1867. Memorials commemorate Sir Henry Edwards MP and voyagers Richard Clark and John Endicott. Clark, a Weymouth captain and pilot, sailed with Sir Humphrey Gilbert in 1583 to establish the first British colony in North America, at St John's, Newfoundland. John Endicott (1588-1665) sailed on the *Abigail* from Weymouth on 20 June 1628 and became the first Governor of the colony established by Plymouth settlers in Massachusetts Bay – which they called New England.

The cast-iron Jubilee Clock, gaudiest of the Esplanade landmarks, commemorates Queen Victoria's 1887 Golden Jubilee.

Greenhill Gardens, to the north, were given to the town in 1897 by Sir Frederick Johnstone to celebrate the Queen's Diamond Jubilee. The Floral Clock dates from 1936 and is made up with more than a thousand plants.

Left – *Jubilee Clock: for Queen Victoria's first 50 years.* Above – *Donkey rides: lasting tradition on Weymouth sands.*

Opening time: for craft entering the Backwater.

63 TOWN BRIDGE

The Town Bridge, across Weymouth Harbour (SY 679 787), is a steel and concrete structure which splits in two to allow convoys of yachts in and out of the marina that occupies the Backwater. It was opened in 1930 by the Duke of York, later King George VI.

The first bridge on the site, replacing a chain ferry, was the 'Timber Bridge' of 1597. There was an innovative successor, as the *John Bull* newspaper reported on 5 January 1823: 'The construction of the new bridge at Weymouth is entirely novel. It is built of stone, with elliptical arches, with a drawbridge centre, upon the principle of Perronet, for the River Neva at St Petersburgh.'

Weymouth's first opening bridge pre-dated London's Tower Bridge by nearly seventy years.

The Backwater: a prosperous sea of parked boats.

64 RADIPOLE LAKE

Close to Weymouth's railway yard, and beside a convenient car-park next to its inner relief road, there is an expanse of sheltered water inland from the Backwater (SY 675 795). This is Radipole Lake which was a tidal estuary until the building of Westham Bridge in 1924. It became a freshwater lagoon and was declared a nature reserve in 1948. Owned by Weymouth Corporation, it is managed by the Royal Society for the Protection of Birds and its reedbeds boast bearded tits, Cetti's warblers, water rails and mute swans, to mention four of more than 50 breeding species. Water rails are secretive and stay in the reeds for a long as possible, into the winter, until a deep-freeze forces them out to feed.

Migrants in the autumn include black tern, yellow wagtail and sand martin. The latter stay to roost. They are followed by black, little and common tern, little gull, little ringed plover, grey plover, little stint, greenshank, and spotted redshank. Lesser known gulls appear, such as the (uncommon) common gull, and glaucous, Iceland, little and Mediterranean gulls.

Rarities have been coming for as long as bird movements have been recorded, notably the pied-bill grebe (first for Britain, 1880-81), green-winged teal (first for Dorset, 1948), and lesser yellowleg (first for Dorset, 1963). Cynics say that Radipole consistently scores because it has more observers than birds. It is so accessible that the moment anything moves there is liable to be a battery of field-glasses on site to note the fact.

Radipole Lake: Weymouth's inner-city bird reserve.

65 NOTTINGTON SPA

The three-storey octagonal pump-room and baths at Nottington Spa (SY 661 824) were built in 1830 over a sulphurous 'Medical Spring'. This had been credited for curing consumption and as the remedy for a wide range of general illness, receiving a royal visit, from Queen Charlotte, in September 1791.

Its well was also used for the dipping of sick cats and dogs. Concern about contamination led to the capping of the spring and its piping into the Spa House and Sulphur Baths. The building is now a private house but the pump is preserved in the basement.

66 LODMOOR COUNTRY PARK

The coastal marshland behind the sea-wall at Lodmoor, including reed-beds and Weymouth's former municipal rubbish tip, is now the 153-acre Lodmoor Country Park (SY 683 808) and managed by RSPB wardens. They regularly log 25 species a day with noteworthy firsts ranging from the American lesser yellowleg, blown 8000 kilometres off course in the autumn of 1993 to the bittern through the winter of 2001-02. It is hoped their boom will be heard as they stay to breed. Rare but relatively reliable as returnees are the little stint and wood sandpiper. Snipe, dunlin and godwit are commoner.

Habitat restoration has included mowing and grazing with the water-level being raised for the benefit of plants and insects as well as the birds. It is all a far cry from drainage and encroachment, including the houses of the closes off Weymouth Bay Avenue, Beaumont Avenue and Grove Avenue. On the other side, towards Overcombe, the incursion of Oakbury Drive and Southdown Avenue now ends at a bird hide where developers once hoped to break through to Radipole.

Seawards, on the edge of the town, attractions include miniature golf and a railway, a model village, the Aquarium and Butterfly Farm, and Sea Life Centre. Preston Beach Road carries the A353 behind the sea wall between Greenhill Gardens and Furzey Cliff.

67 WEYMOUTH SEA-LIFE CENTRE

Weymouth Sea-Life Centre at Greenhill (SY 684 805) was established in 1983 by David Mace, a marine biologist, who opened a similar aquarium at Oban in Scotland the previous year. Giant rays, sharks, conger eels, electric rays and octopus swim around in huge tanks. Pumps in the bay keep the sea-water circulating, across reefs of cockle shells.

The glass viewing points required eight tons of one-inch glass – more than manufacturers Pilkington usually produce in a whole year – and the initial catch for the aquarium included a lamprey, a primitive species, and a blue-backed squat lobster. Weymouth also provided the fish for the first salt-water tanks at London Zoo.

68 JORDAN HILL and BOWLEAZE COVE

Among cliffside houses east of Lodmoor, between Overcombe Drive and New Barn on the north side of Bowleaze Cove Way, the footings of a Roman temple on Jordan Hill have been preserved in a square of grass (SY 699 821). The site was excavated in 1843 and found to have been in use from the first to fourth centuries. Coins, iron swords, pottery, and two Purbeck marble columns were found. A pit at the centre of the courtyard was more than 4½ metres deep and contained what appeared to be votive offerings of numerous bird species including starlings, buzzards, crows and ravens. The latter were sacred to the Celts.

Eastwards, the cul-de-sac promenade leads to Pontin's Holiday Camp, in a huge white painted seaward-facing slab of 1930s leisure architecture. Beyond this mock-Mediterranean statement, nature and geology re-assert themselves on Redcliff Point, a scrubby landslipped headland of oozing grey clay and a mix of sands.

69 OSMINGTON WHITE HORSE

Dorset's one and only equestrian hill figure features King George III riding along what became White Horse Hill above Osmington (SY 716 843). It is the most distinctive landmark of Weymouth Bay and covers an acre of steeply sloping chalk hillside with a fine view over Weymouth's countryside, Portland, and into the English Channel. The whole area of the figure was stripped of turf rather than just its outline.

The figure has been wrongly dated to 1815 by the Royal Commission on Historical Monuments. It was in the course of construction on 19 August 1808 when Weymouth bookseller John Wood sent the antiquary Sir Richard Colt Hoare, at Stourhead House, a drawing of a flanged bronze axe: 'To one of your taste, and knowledge as an antiquarian, I flatter myself that the annexed exact size and representation of an instrument (whether of British, or Roman antiquity) will not prove unacceptable. It was discovered in cutting out an equestrian figure of the King in the side of Osmington Hill. Should any further discoveries be made in this way, I shall feel happy and proud to communicate the same to you.'

Five days later, Thomas Oldfeld Bartlett, returning to Wareham from Weymouth, noted in his diary the 'image cut out presenting King George III on horseback'. This contemporary evidence counters claims for a later date. The classic artistic error is that it shows the King riding away from Weymouth, which would soon cause derision, and is said to have caused the principal designer to kill himself. The project was financed by Weymouth businessman John Rainier.

70 OSMINGTON MILLS

The visit of landscape painter John Constable (1776-1837) to Osmington Mills (SY 735 818) led to a series of sketches that blossomed into his major study entitled

Osmington sunset: redolent of Constable's Weymouth Bay painting.

'Osmington Shore, near Weymouth'. It looks that way, to Redcliff Point, and resulted from his six-week honeymoon at Osmington Vicarage. John had married Maria Elizabeth Bicknell on 2 October 1816, in a service conducted by their friend Rev. John Fisher (1787-1832), who was vicar of Osmington and prebendary of Sarum.

Public viewing of the largish painting was at the British Institute in 1819 but the critic for the *New Monthly Magazine* showed little enthusiasm. 'Not a very happy performance,' he declared, 'but a sketch of barren sand without interest, and very unlike the artist's other pleasing work of home scenery.'

Neither Constable or Fisher regarded the Dorset coast with equanimity. Its remarkable red sunsets over Weymouth Bay were a terrible beauty. For them there was desolation and tragedy.

The Fishers lost a cousin, Captain John Wordsworth, when his ship, the *Abergavenny*, sank off Portland with 200 men on 5 February 1805. The captain's brother was William Wordsworth who commemorated the mariner, at the helm of an East Indiaman, with his poem *The Happy Warrior*. Though ostensibly about the death of Nelson, later that year, it draws on John's life and character and refers to Portland with a line about 'The seas in agony, and that dismal shore'.

David Lucas produced an engraving of the Constable before the canvas left the country, for France, where it now hangs in the Louvre. Mills Road still ends with a characterful cluster of buildings including the Cottage, the Dell, Coastguard House and the thatched Smugglers Inn, which used to be called the Picnic Inn. A chalet-style tearoom defiantly rides the penultimate wave of landslipped cliff. Eastwards is the steel skeleton of the steamer *Minx* which rammed the shore in 1929.

Below left – *Smugglers Inn: nestling in the hollow at Osmington Mills.* Below – *Deserted slipway: the rugged shore at Osmington Mills.*

71 UPTON FORT

One of the country's more unusual holiday homes, set into the cliffs between Osmington Mills and Ringstead Bay (SY 742 816), was shown to me by Dr John Pinsent. The iron plaque on three feet of solid concrete was to Edward VII: 'E. R. 1902'. Dr Pinsent was at home in one great, long room, with brick vaulting springing off bunk-room girders. His current bedtime reading were proofs for a new edition of his book *Greek Mythology*.

It was the operations room for the mainland gun crews who watched the approaches to Portland Harbour. Upton Fort was carefully sited on a man-made shelf cut into the cliffside slope so that the big guns did not break the skyline. These commanded the deep-water passage into Portland that runs beside the shallows of the Lulworth Grounds and then crosses Weymouth Bay. Their field of fire was south-south-west over Bran Ledge and Perry Ledge.

Coast battery: saw action against German gunboats, beside Ringstead Bay.

The 12-inch guns were supplied from two magazines with lifts and hoists, from 6 metres below ground. Two smaller, 6-inch batteries, also survive and the fort remained in commission, against E-boats – intruding German gunboats – until 1945. The War Office relinquished ownership which reverted to the Pomeroy family of Spring Bottom, Osmington, who are said to have been paid £400 for the land, by the Admiralty, in 1900.

72 RINGSTEAD BAY and BURNING CLIFF

The closest access point to the coast above and below South Down Farm, Sea Barn and the Burning Cliff at Ringstead Bay is from a car-park on National Trust land (SY 760 823). Having turned south from the A353 between Osmington and Warmwell Cross roundabout, beside a wood at Upton, one follows the 3-kilometre lane to the crest of a down overlooking the sea. Paths are signed to the Burning Cliff and Ringstead Bay, in 800 metres, and uphill to the top of White Nothe 1½ kilometres.

Below, west of Ringstead Bay, a succession of ledges remind us that this is a dangerous stretch of coast. Hannah's Ledge, Frenchman's Ledge, Pool Ledge, Bran Ledge, Perry Ledge and Ringstead Ledge take some of their names from shipwrecks. Ringstead Bay then offers a 1½ kilometre-long shingle beach.

Ringstead Bay: dominated by nose-shaped White Nothe.

Westwards, humps and ditches mark the site of the lost mediaeval Ringstead village (SY 747 815). Bigger mounds in the trees are Cold War fall-out shelters of a United States Air Force ultra short-wave communications station. The former Ringstead chapel, now Glebe Cottage (SY 747 817) is beside a bungalow in the next arm of woodland, on the north side of the village site. The chancel and its arch survive from a building first mentioned in 1227. Burials and pieces of dressed stone have been uncovered in the ground to the south.

Modern Ringstead is strung along the flat ground behind the main beach. Holworth is older but has been re-arranged by landslips. Two acres, with a fisherman's cottage, its occupants and their vegetable patch, slid 9 metres in March 1815. They carried on moving over the next three years to within a short distance of the sea. The gooseberry and currant bushes flourished in the mobile garden which, with the cottage, came to a halt on the brow of 'an immense body of cliff'.

The central area above Ringstead Bay, between Rose Cottage and Holworth House, became a tourist attraction for Weymouth visitors when it caught fire in 1826. A booklet describing the occurrence, which continued for three years, was sold in nearby Baggs' Cottage. *Observations on Holworth Cliff* is subtitled as 'containing Local Particulars illustrative and explanatory of the Extraordinary Phenomenon of Sub-terraneous Fire, existing within its interior recesses'.

Its memory is preserved as the Burning Cliff though it is now covered with trees and scrub. Seawards, on a grassy knoll, stands the cabin-church of St Catherine by the Sea, with a dramatic landslipped graveyard. It was built, in timber, in 1906 and refurbished in 1926. Going back to monastic times, Holworth was a detached part of Milton Abbas parish, which also has a St Catherine's Chapel.

In the pastures above, the thatched Sea Barn has been restored by the National Trust, which owns 454 acres beside Ringstead Bay. This includes the 273-acre South Down Farm which was transferred to the Trust through the National Land Fund – in memory of the dead of the Second World War – in 1949. It stretches inland to Bascombe Barn and the foot of the escarpment at Moigns Down. The remaining 107 acres of White Nothe undercliff were bought with Enterprise Neptune funds in 1968 and 74 acres at Sea Barn Farm added in 1984 through various bequests and grants.

73 WHITE NOTHE COTTAGES

Brick-built on the 495-feet chalk headland in the early nineteenth century, as a row of Coastguard Cottages, these are the highest buildings on the Dorset coast (SY 773 809). They are on the Chaldon Herring side of the parish boundary with Owermoigne with a panoramic view over Ringstead Bay, Weymouth Bay and Portland. The spot remains a boundary and is now the south-west extremity of the area of Purbeck District Council.

The original 'Nore' name of the headland became 'Nose' in Dorset speech, and was promoted in print by the headland's best known occupant, topographical author Llewelyn Powys (1884-1939). It is, he argued, nose-like in profile, and the description 'White Nothe or White Nose' appeared on the 6-inch Ordnance map of 1903. He cited Thomas Hardy who said that in profile it was the Duke of Wellington's nose. To me

Highest houses: former Coastguard Cottages on White Nothe.

it's not that different from Hardy's. These days, however, 'White Nose' has become a lost cause and is regarded as affectation.

74 MOONFLEET ZIG-ZAG

The track down the 500-feet chalk headland at White Nothe (SY 773 808), to the rocky foreshore, is a public path but the National Trust says 'it is too dangerous for walkers'. The narrow grassy path zig-zags between and over the outcrops and was brought to lasting fame by author and armaments manufacturer John Meade Falkner for the climax – the escape scene – in his Victorian smuggling classic, *Moonfleet*:

'Just at the end of this flat ledge, furthest from where the bridle-path leads down, but not a hundred yards from where we stand, there is a sheep-track leading up the cliff. It starts where the under-cliff dies back again into the chalk face, and climbs by slants and elbow-turns up to the top. The shepherds call it the Zig-Zag, and even sheep lose their footing on it; and of men I never heard but one had climbed it, and that was Lander Jordan, when the Excise was on his heels, half a century back

'And 'twas a task that might cow the bravest, and when I looked upon the Zig-Zag, it seemed better to stay where we were and fall upon the rocks below. For the Zig-Zag started off as a fair enough chalk path, but in a few paces narrowed down till it was

White Nothe: 495-feet start for Dorset's white cliffs.

but a whiter thread against the grey-white cliff-face, and afterwards turned sharply back, crossing a hundred feet direct above our heads. And then I smelt an evil stench, and looking about, saw the blown-out carcass of a rotting sheep lie close at hand.'

Navigation beacon: one of the pair on The Warren.

75 NAVIGATION BEACONS and FOUNTAIN ROCK

Two concrete Beacons, in the shape of sharply pointed pyramids (SY 782 809), line-up as navigation markers to correct approach across Weymouth Bay for the East Ship Channel into Portland Harbour.

Below, the vertical chalk outcrop of Fountain Rock rises like a column from the inaccessible breach below, and surrounding south-facing coastal downland is for much of the year alive with butterflies and their flowering food plants. Fountain Rock was the favourite place of Weymouth author Dr Llewellyn Pridham.

76 LLEWELYN POWYS'S GRAVE

The ashes of Dorset author and essayist Llewelyn Powys lie beneath a four-feet block of Portland stone below the fence-line between the Beacons (SY 783 810). It was carved and inscribed by sculptor Elizabeth Muntz from his home village of East Chaldon and put in place when Defence Regulations were relaxed to allow access to the coast after the Second World War: 'Llewelyn Powys. 3 August 1884, 2 December 1939. The living. The living. He shall praise thee.'

Paying homage: Llewelyn Powys's otherwise lonely grave.

77 BAT'S HEAD and BUTTER ROCK

Bat's Head is a perpendicular chalk cliff, up to 200 feet high, projecting south from The Warren between Fountain Rock and Durdle Door (SY 796 803). It is perforated at sea-level by a small arch.

Below left – *Chalk cliffs: from Bat's Head to Durdle Door.* Below – *Chalk cliffs: Bat's Head and Butter Rock.*

Low sun: going down in the west, behind Bat's Head.

To the east, in the usually sheltered corner towards Swyre Head, is a chalk stack known as Butter Rock (though the name has currently dropped off the Ordnance map). These are the most westward examples of text-book landform geology that unfold along the next 5 kilometres of the coast path to Lulworth Cove.

78 DURDLE DOOR

Forming the projecting western end of a bastion of upturned Purbeck stone, with breaches through to the chalk on either side of it, Durdle Door (SY 805 802) is a vertical example of what Lulworth Cove demonstrates on the horizontal plane. It is open to the southerly gales and a little bay is developing on the landward side, between it and the cliffs of Newlands Warren, and a string of offshore rocks extends further west for 1½ kilometres. These carry bovine names (being from west to east The Calf, The Cow, The Blind Cow and The Bull).

'Durdle' is derived from the Old English word 'thyrel', or 'thirl', meaning 'holed'. Initial 'th' sounds are pronounced as 'd' in the Dorset dialect.

Beach view: breakers coming through Durdle Door.

79 MAN O' WAR COVE and NEWLANDS FARM

The next example of coastal erosion, opening out from behind a line of offshore rocks, is Man o' War Cove (SY 807 803). Its saucer-shaped beach is growing at the expense of the bowl in the chalk cliffs towards Newlands Farm and its caravan camp. Each year there are fresh slicks of milky white water to betray continuing slippages.

Man o' War Cove, another name lost from the maps, may have been coined as a description for the shape of its principal rock. On the other hand, it may well have claimed a warship, to add to its tally of shipwrecks. These cliffs feature as Dagger's Grave, inspired by an actual Dagger's Gate, in Thomas Hardy's 1879 tale *The Distracted Preacher*.

Newlands Farm, an eighteenth-century house with rustic outbuildings, came to notoriety as the favourite holiday haunt of the promiscuous philosopher and mathematician Bertrand Russell (1872-1970). He brought his series of lovers here, sometimes as a harem, for two decades. Lady Ottoline Morrell (a Liberal MP's wife), in 1916, was soon joined by Colette O'Neil (Lady Constance Malleson), Dora Black, Katherine Mansfield, Vivien Eliot (first wife of T. S. Eliot), Dorothy Wrinch, and Patricia 'Peter' Spence.

80 ST OSWALD'S BAY and DUNGY HEAD

St Oswald's Bay opens out towards Dungy Head where the string of desirable homes in Britwell Drive, west of Lulworth Cove, end in a jumbled undercliff of chalk and harder rocks (SY 816 800). The inland peak, at 453 feet, is the rounded barrow-topped summit of Hambury Tout.

Between Dungy Head and Hambury Tout runs the wide white line of what may well be the busiest public footpath in the British Isles. Only one in a thousand users will stray off towards either the headland or the hill. The flow is between the twin honeypots of Lulworth Cove and Durdle Door.

Dungy Head: in line with the rocks of Man o'War Cove.

81 STAIR HOLE

The perforations in the cliff and crumpled strata beside it make Stair Hole the ultimate location for an outdoor geology lesson (SY 822 798). For much of the time you can listen and learn about the 'Lulworth crumple'. The bowl-shaped depression acts as a sound box when a teacher shouts to an impatient herd. You will hear that the collision of the Earth's tectonic plates left these visible waves in the rock where firmer and harder Portland stone rucked up the Middle and Upper Purbeck beds.

Their subsequent exposure is the story of erosion, with the sea having broken through gashes in these rocks, to wash away soft beds of Wealden sands and clay.

Contorted strata: the famous Lulworth crumple, beside Stair Hole.

82 LULWORTH COVE

The frying-pan-shaped inlet at Lulworth Cove (SY 824 799) displays the erosion process writ large, with an appealing example of natural symmetry that casts a picturesque stone against the chaos theory of the universe. What has happened is that a breach in the outer stone wall, behind which a watercourse had scooped out softer Wealden deposits, was then contained by semi-hard chalk beds.

Lulworth Cove: semi-landlocked behind the rocks.

There used to be a limekiln and stone pier in the north-west corner of the Cove, of which only odd stones remain, and oyster beds on the western side. More recently, from late Victorian times until the 1960s, and again with nostalgic returns of the *Waverley*, paddle-steamers have brought visitors. Hostelries include the Lulworth Cove Hotel and the Mill House Hotel. The Doll's House, a miniature stone-roofed cottage, is now a fishing museum.

The best known literary visitors was the poet John Keats (1795-1821), for his last hours on English soil on 30 September 1820, when he was a dying man, outward bound for Rome in the *Maria Crowther* for Rome. It was while waiting at Lulworth for a favourable wind that he is said to have written his final poem, the sonnet 'Bright star, would I were steadfast as thou art'.

Oddly, without his knowing of the coincidence at the time, Great War poet Rupert Brooke (1887-1915) dropped his copy of Keats from a boat, into rocks at Lulworth Cove. He stayed in rooms above the post office, having discovered Lulworth in 1907, while staying with his maiden aunts in Bournemouth: 'Tomorrow I'm going to the most beautiful place in England to work. It is called West Lulworth.'

Thomas Hardy wrote a centenary poem for the Keats visit, in 1920, asking 'Do you see that man' and answering:

'That man goes to Rome – to death, despair;
And no one notes him now but you and I:
A hundred years and the world will follow him there,
And head with reverence where his ashes lie.'

Hardy embraced Lulworth Cove in his works, calling it Lulwind Cove, and made it the location for the decisive moment in *Far from the Madding Crowd* (1874) when Sergeant Francis 'Frank' Troy leaves his clothes on the beach and fakes his own drowning. *A Tradition of 1804* (1882) records the tradition that Napoleon Bonaparte visited the Cove and decided, wisely, against invading here.

Napoleon's Grande Armée was concentrated around Boulogne, opposite Kent, and though the French ebb-tide would bring it westwards the English flood tide would tend to do a Caesar and William the Conqueror and bring it back eastwards. It would also be pushed up-Channel by prevailing south-westerly winds. Even if Napoleon was thinking of landing points to the west the great sandy beaches of Poole Bay would have been a much more accessible proposition. The French had centuries of knowledge of the English coast and its defences and were accustomed to sending corsairs to capture fishermen and peasants for interrogation.

That is the case against. On the other hand, it would be in character for Napoleon to take a day off to enjoy a few relatively safe steps on English soil, rather than risking a visit to areas alert to the threat from 10,000 craft that were being prepared to carry 100,000 men. There could have been a plan for a diversionary attack to draw the English fleet down-Channel in the direction of Dorset where Napoleon was keeping up the pressure, from Brest and Cherbourg, for this express purpose. It had an effect, as George III showed in June 1804, when he told the Duke of York: 'Dorset is one of the most vulnerable parts of the kingdom.'

83 LITTLE BINDON and PEPLER'S POINT

The Cistercian community of Bindon Abbey was founded by the sea, on the east side of Lulworth Cove (SY 831 798) in about 1150, and moved from there to an inland site at Wool in 1172. The monks took the name Bindon with them and the ruins of the second Bindon Abbey stand in wooded grounds beside the River Frome.

A Victorian map shows the 'Site of Bindon Abbey' in the overgrown vale immediately north-east of the present Little Bindon cottage but modern maps no longer show its location. The chapel-cum-cottage dates from 1250 and was taken over and re-roofed by rabbit warreners in 1500. Brick dressings date from the 1700s. A twelfth-century carving from the original Bindon Abbey was reset in the east wall.

The cottage became the rural hideaway of eminent town planner Sir George Lionel Pepler (1882-1959) for more than half a century. His memorial is a stone seat on Pepler's Point (SY 828 796), the promontory named for him above the eastern entrance to Lulworth Cove, where we read how 'he loved the land of England . . . and Dorset best of all'. There is nothing to tell us that he devised the country's original network of arterial roads in 1914 and received his knighthood in 1948 for drafting the Town and Country Planning Act.

84 THE FOSSIL FOREST

The Fossil Forest is a line of fern-like cycad tree stumps on a slanting ledge directly above the sea to the east of Lulworth Cove, accessible only when the Army unlocks its Lulworth Range Walks (SY 832 797). The three best trunks are at the eastern extremity of what is more of a shelter belt than a forest. Reaching them involves some clambering across rocks.

They are 2 to 3 metres in diameter and hollow at the core. One pair are only 3 metres apart. All would have grown upright but are now at an angle, tilting inland at about

Heavy seas: crashing against the Fossil Forest.

Cycad trees: the ferns of the Fossil Forest.

45 degrees, as a result of subsequent upheaval of the strata. Fossilised wood has been found in newly discovered specimens, as on Portland in 2001, but the Fossil Forest merely contains the shapes of the trees in hardened calcareous tufa.

A notice explains: 'Many of the rocks of Purbeck began as sediments accumulating 120 million years ago in swamps. As the soils gradually built up, large pine-like and fern-like trees grew here. Some of these stumps became fossilised, but only the former positions of the stumps, covered by a lime-type deposit, can be seen. The Fossil Forest is part of a site of special scientific interest. It is an important part of our heritage and deserves your care, consideration and protection.'

85 MUPE BAY and SMUGGLERS' CAVE

The most extensive string of offshore rocks on the Dorset coast, jagged and triangular in profile, Mupe Rocks and the boulder-strewn Mupe Bay comprise one of the most breathtaking spots reached by the Lulworth Range Walks (SY 842 797). Tucked away at the western end of Mupe's second little cove is a genuine Smugglers' Cave (named as such on the Ordnance map, with the correct apostrophe for plural use). This used

Left – *Mupe Rocks and Worbarrow Bay.* Above – *Mupe Rocks: from the pebble beach.*

to be known as Bacon Hole and has the ruins of a winch-house on the clifftop, directly above, beside the concrete lines of a wartime pill-box.

Smugglers' Cave is 12 metres deep and 7½ metres wide. What is remarkable about it is a false-wall, about 2½ metres high, built across its back end. This encloses a chamber 4½ metres wide by 3 metres deep. There are the remains of a door, which could easily have been concealed by rocks.

North of these hard and tilting outcrops of Purbeck stone come a band of multi-coloured Wealden sands and clays. Chalk cliffs form the broader backdrop.

86 COCKPIT HEAD and ARISH MELL GAP

Another of the cliffs no longer given its name on the Ordnance map, Cockpit Head (SY 847 802) rises sheer and conical to 400 feet above Worbarrow Bay. It is the eastern end of the chalk spine of Bindon Hill and only accessible when the Lulworth Range Walks are open.

Arish Mell: between Flower's Barrow and Cockpit Head.

Below, to the east, the cliff path swiftly drops to sea-level in the Arish Mell Gap. Inland, towards Lulworth Castle, Sea Vale forms a wide valley between Lulworth Camp and the Purbeck Hills.

87 FLOWER'S BARROW

Entrenching the western end of the Purbeck Hills where they give their name to Rings Hill the ramparts of Flower's Barrow (SY 865 805) now form the central peak of the Lulworth Range Walks. Along the southern side, however, banks were unnecessary as the cliffs fall 550 feet into Worbarrow Bay. Much of the Iron Age hill-fort has gone the same way as fissures open between dense tussocks of grass and eventually slip over the edge.

The fortifications date from about 50 BC. There are strong double banks along the landward approaches, with the spaces between these at the west and east ends having been stretched to keep an advantage with the defenders. The latter on the inside bank would stand six feet higher than any attacker who had broken through the ditch and climbed the palisade on to the outer rampart. A precisely engineered mathematical answer to the matter of height over distance was the to key to slingstone warfare. Both sides would catapult beach pebbles at each other until the 2nd Roman Legion, Augusta, brought blitzkrieg storming techniques and overran the Durotrigic strongholds after the invasion of 43 AD.

Defensive line: Iron Age bank at Flower's Barrow, reused for a wartime pillbox.

88 WORBARROW BAY and WORBARROW TOUT

Lulworth has seen mechanised live-firing since the first tanks in the Great War and Tyneham parish, including Worbarrow hamlet (SY 871 797), was requisitioned in the Second World War to train tank crews for the Allied invasion of Normandy. The parishioners were evacuated on 19 December 1943. Despite a pledge that they could return, the homes are now ruins or less, and Worbarrow is only accessible, along a 1½ kilometre-long track from Tyneham car-park (SY 882 802), when the road into the valley (SY 895 816) is open for the Lulworth Range Walks.

Worbarrow's working tenants were the Miller family of fishermen. Their three cottages, in stunning beach-side settings, are now reduced to a few walls. The scenery has fared better, with multi-coloured Wealden sands rising behind into immense chalk cliffs, and the sugar-loaf shape of Worbarrow Tout thrusts far into Worbarrow Bay. Tucked away on the eastern side is the rocky inlet of Pondfield Cove.

Top – *Wealden sands: contrasting with the whiteness of Flower's Barrow.* Above – *Pondfield Cove: a tiny inlet between the rocks of Worbarrow Tout and Gad Cliff.* Right – *Worbarrow Tout: the western end of the Purbeck marble beds.*

Worbarrow Tout is the western extremity of the Purbeck marble beds. Not truly a marble, this is hard grey freshwater limestone, which lends itself to carving and takes a polish. Most was extracted from around Langton Matravers, and exported via Corfe Castle from Ower Quay, for the post-Norman building of cathedrals and palaces across the land. It is accompanied towards the end of Worbarrow Tout by deposits of gypsum. These also had their uses, being ground to a powder in Roman times and used to pack lead-lined Christian graves in the big cemetery at Poundbury, Dorchester.

89 GAD CLIFF and WAGON ROCK

The 1½ kilometre-long ribbon of limestone crags at Gad Cliff (SY 884 797) rises 481 feet above the sea with a wild undercliff and then tilts landward with grassy pastures that drop down to the main path at Tyneham. 'Gad' takes its name from a quarryman's wedge and perfectly describes its angular shape. There is short cut to it from the village car-park but this and the cliff path are only usable when the Lulworth Range Walks are accessible.

Breeding birds include peregrine falcons and ravens, which continued in residence on these Army-lands when agricultural chemicals wiped them out elsewhere in Dorset, though sea-birds continue to decline from a combination of factors including over-fishing, pollution and recurrent severe storms.

Wagon Rock is prominent beside the foreshore where Philip Draper pointed out to me a smugglers' hiding hole in 1969. Six smugglers were apprehended on the cliff above on 31 January 1834, and were sentenced to death, but this was commuted to hard labour for a year in each case. There is no longer any lawful access to the undercliff.

Stone cliffs: the ridge from Gad Cliff, across Worbarrow Tout, to Mupe Rocks beyond.

90 TYNEHAM CAP and BRANDY BAY

The great tumbling seascape below the 549-feet conical summit of Tyneham Cap can only be visited, from the village car-park (SY 882 802) when the Lulworth Range Walks are open.

Brandy Bay, and all the coastal slopes below the yellow markers of the cliff path, are permanently off-limits, though there is spectacular view from the notices warning of unstable cliffs. Given that it is also the inaccessible over-shoot zone for the tank firing ranges in this instance the restriction to visual access is understandable.

Left – *Tyneham Cap: a 549-feet summit between the cliffs and Tyneham House.*

91 BROAD BENCH

Shale ledges begin to the west of Kimmeridge Bay with a distinctive example, known as Broad Bench (SY 898 788), which is very different from the rest. They are irregular and jagged whereas Broad Bench is regular. It comprises a sea-level shelf, 200 metres square, projecting seawards from a similar sized chunk of softer clay cliff that has a flat top about 50 feet above. A steel bung marks the site of a sealed oilwell.

Broad Bench lies between Hobarrow Bay and Charnel. The cliff path, at the eastern end of the Lulworth Range Walks, by-passes the headland though it can be approached across the rocks from Kimmeridge Bay at low tide.

Charnel beach: the western corner of Kimmeridge Bay.

92 CHARNEL and KIMMERIDGE BAY

The hollow at Charnel near the western end of Kimmeridge Bay (SY 901 791), in the parish of Tyneham, enjoyed brief fame as Kimmeridge Lifeboat Station. It was established in 1868 after a series of shipwrecks along this shore and had William Stickland, from Stickland's Cottage, South Egliston, as its first coxswain. He steered the 8½ metre *Mary Heape* through ferocious seas on the night of 8 December 1872 to rescue 17 Norwegian crewmen from the *Stralsund* after she wedged on the Kimmeridge Ledges.

Two more lifeboats saw service at Kimmeridge but the station had its limitations, due to the distance between far-flung dwellings on this sparsely populated shore, and was closed due to shortage of manpower in 1896. Louis Stickland turned the shed and slipway into a boat-building yard but the site is now a grassy gully.

On the cliff above, in the coastal salient of Steeple parish, the 'nodding donkey' or pump-jack oilwell has been a familiar landmark beside the cliff path since British Petroleum struck black gold in 1959. It was then regarded as a small-scale operation, and would be just that in comparison with the huge oil-field discovered beneath Wytch Farm, Corfe Castle, in 1973. Though on shale cliffs it extracts its sulphur-free light crude from the Cornbrash limestone at 545 metres below. On 21 October 1968 it became the first British oilwell to produce 100,000 tons of crude; all of it taken out by road tankers, which then went to Wareham for onward progress by rail to Ellesmere Port, Cheshire. It has since exceeded 500,000 tons and the oil now goes to the rail-head at Furzebrook.

Industry at Kimmeridge Bay (SY 909 791) goes back as far as anywhere on the Dorset coast. The story begins with hand-cut imitation jet armlets, in shale, made through the Iron Age from 400 BC onwards. In the Roman period the process was mechanised and bracelets were lathe-turned in quantity. This a left a peculiar waste product in the form of thousands of waste cores, each circular with square holes, which puzzled antiquaries took to be currency and dubbed as 'coal money'.

The remains of substantial pieces of ornately carved claw-feet shale tables and other furniture in Kimmeridge 'blackstone' have been found at villa sites. The closest are the Roman villa at Preston and the Town House, Dorchester, but they must have been the height of fashion as similar pieces have been found from Bath and Caerleon in the west to Foscott, Buckinghamshire, and Rothley, Lincolnshire, on the other side of the country. Like all Kimmeridge shale products they would have needed regular polishing, with light oil, to keep them glossy. The natural tendency for shale is to dry and crumble but the longevity of Kimmeridge tables drew Roman furniture expert J. Liversidge to conclude that 'they must have been treasured in Roman-British homes, and handed down from generation to generation as heirlooms'.

Gaulter Gap: dragon's teeth obstacle of a wartime tank-trap overlooked by the Clavell Tower.

The Romans also boiled sea-water at Kimmeridge to produce salt. There is a deposit over a metre thick of broken brick-like clay containers, used for salt boiling, just above the high water mark at the southern end of the bay. This debris represents the inevitable breakages but I have an intact container found in Purbeck. This ceramic vessel has a perforated colander-style capping with a high rim rising from it. Water would be poured in and boiled away in a continuous process until it was filled to the cap. Then it would have been shipped and sold in a distribution system that not only reached London but also supplied the legions on Hadrian's Wall.

The evidence of eight centuries of enterprise ended with the Saxons and Kimmeridge Bay was known as Botteridge Pool during the Middle Ages. Industry resumed in the 1560s when Lord Mountjoy discovered 'alum shale' yielded the double sulphate of aluminium and potassium which was widely used in medicine and the arts. By 1600, the alum works were operated by Sir William Clavell whose 'houses, furnaces and cole pitts' would be seized and ransacked after a group of London merchants had been granted King James I's sole patent for making alum. He had built 'a little key in imitation of that at Lime' – the Cobb at Lyme Regis – which fell into a disrepair and was eventually swept way in 1745.

Clavell went from alum to glass-making. With Abraham Bigo, from 1617, he made green drinking glass on a site towards the south side of the bay, just north of the fishermen's huts. That led to a dispute with Admiral Sir Robert Mansel, whose staff were 'seduced' southwards from Newcastle to Kimmeridge, and Clavell died in 1644 without having recovered his financial position.

Industry resumed at Kimmeridge in 1848 when the Bituminous Shale Company extracted shale which was shipped to Weymouth and used for by-products including varnish, grease, pitch, naphtha, dyes, wax and fertiliser. Parliament authorised 'railways, inclined planes, causeways' in 1847 and these were built across the top of Hen Cliff to Cuddle.

The following year Wanostrocht and Company, from its works at Northport, Wareham, was lighting the town's lamps and its new railway station with Kimmeridge shale-gas. Ferguson and Muschamp also established a plant on the site that became Wareham Pottery at Sandford.

German chemist August Wilhelm von Hofmann (1818-92) experimented with Kimmeridge shale in 1857 and produced a favourable analysis of 11,300 cubic feet of gas per ton (compared with 12,000 for coal) providing good quality illumination and useful by-products. It led to Wanostrocht's winning the contract to light the streets of Paris in 1858. Their 1860-built stone pier extended westward from the ledge at the southern extremity of Kimmeridge Bay.

Wareham Oil and Candle Company was the next producer, from 1862 until it was wiped out by a fire, at Wareham, in 1872. The Kimmeridge operation had already moved sideways to Cornwall. The West of England Fireclay Bitumen and Chemical Company claimed in 1871 to be shipping 10,000 tons of Kimmeridge shale each year to its works at Calstock for conversion into between 320,000 and 400,000 gallons of heavy yellow shale oil. It also won a contract for sending 10,000 tons of shale to King's Cross, London.

The Mansfield Shaft of 1883, midway between Cuddle D-Plantation and Clavell's Hard, was named for Charles Blachford Mansfield (1815-55), pioneer of the coal tar industry, who met his end from burns at the Paris Exhibition when a naphtha still overflowed as he prepared 'benzol' specimens (now known as benzene). A wooden pier was built to the north of Wanostrocht's pier, stretching north-westwards into the bay, and a railway laid from it to points at a junction 450 metres east of Kimmeridge Coastguard Station. This served another 'Level' of extraction, to the south, and the main track snaked up the hollow to the Mansfield Shaft, 700 metres further southwards. A total of 5000 feet of tunnels were dug during the next seven years, by the Kimmeridge Oil and Carbon Company Limited, according to the maps of the final stage of its operations in 1890. These extended south-eastwards, to beyond Clavell's Hard, and one was still accessible to foolhardy cliffside adventurers in the late twentieth century.

There was a burning cliff here in 1973, reviving accounts of that beside Ringstead Bay, caused by oxidation of pyrite in the oil shale. Temperatures upwards of 500 degrees centigrade were recorded and the cliff smoked, through the autumn and into

December, through vertical cracks from underground. Beachcombed timber had been pushed into fissures and was also smouldering. Strong sulphur dioxide fumes induced dizziness. Having been singed bare the exposed clifftop north-west of Clavell's Hall changed in colour from grey to orange.

Rock flora: the waters of Kimmeridge Bay are a marine nature reserve.

93 KIMMERIDGE MARINE NATURE RESERVE

The current marine life of the Jurassic Coast can be viewed on the shelving ledges of Kimmeridge Bay, courtesy live on-site television coverage provided by Dorset Wildlife Trust, into a beach-side interpretation centre (SY 909 788). Established in 1978, this was the first marine nature reserve to be designated beside the British mainland, after a successful offshore project around Lundy Island.

Its £100,000 centre, replacing a former fisherman's hut, was designed by Wareham town planner David Morgan and built by Ryan Build of Swanage in 2001. Closed-circuit monitoring of sealife and the colourful underwater kelp flora is backed by a mass of information from other sensors. These maintain a constant health-check on the vitality of the water and record temperature, salinity, sediment levels in suspension, and surface turbulence. The data-base reflects meteorological and seasonal fluctuations and may also indicate wider aspects of climate change. Some species are declining but others will arrive if warming continues.

Below left – *Winter sunset: south-westwards, into Weymouth Bay, silhouetting Broad Bench.* Below – *Kimmeridge Bay: mining its grey oil-bearing shale was once a major industry.*

'This is part of an increasing interest nationally in voluntary marine conservation, in interpreting our coast, and in building-up a data-base,' said Trust director Malcolm Macleod. 'It will help us to have a better understanding of life beneath the waves and on the seashore.'

The reserve manager is Peter Tinsley. His work also has an educational dimension. An average of one school group a day explores Kimmeridge Bay. It is also a magnet for unsupervised youngsters. Notices and leaflets emphasise the importance of vulnerable species such as limpets and ask children to desist from disturbing their homes. Young crab-fishers are asked to return their catches to the water.

94 CLAVELL TOWER and CLAVELL'S HARD

The Clavell Tower, a cliff-top folly, was built by Rev. John Richards on Hen Cliff (SY 908 787) in 1831. Richards inherited the Smedmore Estate in 1817, assumed its family name of Clavell, and died in 1833. His circular tower is a three-storey lookout of brick and stone rubble faced with ashlar and stucco. It is surrounded by a colonnade. Having been adopted by the nearby Coastguard Station it had a flag-pole in Victorian and Edwardian times and a collection of discarded cannon set in the surrounding ground.

Colonnaded columns: the Clavell Tower is a clifftop gem.

As the cliff-edge advances, a leaning or collapsing tower has become a real possibility, and an appeal has been launched to fund protection measures.

South-eastwards, in 1400 metres, Clavell's Hard was the landing beach beneath the 172-feet shale cliffs (SY 922 778). Though there is still a sheltered corner it no longer has a beach and there is now no way down. It is neither usable or accessible.

Offshore, the notorious Kimmeridge Ledges jut south-eastwards in a series of parallel bands, reaching a visible maximum of 300 metres off Rope Lake Head (SY 927 776). Their underwater presence extends much further and has claimed a tally of shipwrecks over the centuries that is second only to that of the Chesil Beach and Portland.

95 SWYRE HEAD and ELDON SEAT

The 666-feet headland of Swyre Head is a kilometre inland (SY 935 785). Dominating the coastline from Kimmeridge Bay to St Alban's Head, it is the highest point in the Isle of Purbeck, marginally out-topping the whole of the Purbeck Hills. On top of the escarpment, on plateau downland, is an 2½ metre-high Bronze Age burial mound. Swyre, a recurrent placename along the Dorset coast, is recorded from before 1590 and has its origin in a late West Saxon word for a promontory.

Eldon Seat, to the south-east, is a block of Purbeck stone 2½ metres long and just over a metre wide, with another massive ashlar as the back-rest, set on a raised podium (SY

Kimmeridge coast: Smedmore is overlooked by the highest point in Purbeck.

Left – *Triple peaks: Swyre Head (left) and Houns-tout Cliff from Emmetts Hill.*

Eldon Seat: Lady Elizabeth Repton laid its first stone, in 1835.

938 779). It has a delightful view of the sheltered mini-landscape of the Big Wood and the lake across to Encombe House, nestling in its Golden Bowl. John Scott, 1st Earl of Eldon (1751-1838), its famous owner, was Lord High Chancellor of England.

The first stone at Eldon Seat was laid by Lady Elizabeth Repton on 13 October 1835. Beside it is a memorial to Pincher, the late Lord Chancellor Eldon's last dog, a German spaniel who outlived his master by two years. Pincher was left an annuity – £8 a year – in Lord Eldon's will.

South-eastwards, in 900 metres, the stream from Encombe Gwyle pours over the cliff and into the sea as a waterfall at Freshwater (SY 944 772). Steps southwards from the coastal path, which used to lead to an iron ladder, now end with a precipice.

96 HOUNS-TOUT CLIFF and CHAPMAN'S POOL

The shale formations of Houns-tout Cliff, capped with yellowish exposures of Purbeck stone at 500 feet, overlook the cove of Chapman's Pool (SY 952 773). The undercliff of Molly's Garden projects seawards at Egmont Point. Eastwards, topped with limestone crags upwards of 400 feet, Emmetts Hill has the viewpoint Royal Marines Monument (SY 959 768).

Above – *Marine's memorial: on Emmetts Hill, overlooking Chapman's Pool.* Right – *Chapman's Pool: Houns-tout Cliff and Broad Bench, from Emmetts Hill.*

Chapman's Pool is not a safe anchorage. The stone-roofed boathouse below Emmetts Hill was built for Chapman's Pool Lifeboat Station. It opened in 1866 after 'great loss of life and property on this part of the coast have at length aroused the attention of the Government' but was soon forced to close when it became obvious that its approaches were liable to be hazardous or impossible in severe weather.

On Egmont Point rocks, in lashing rain and horrendous seas on 10 January 1920, Worth Matravers' curate Rev. Malcolm Piercy and fisherman Frank Lander rescued seven exhausted survivors of the freighter *Treveal*. Her crew had abandoned ship after hitting the Kimmeridge Ledges and the other 36 mariners were drowned. Though split in two, *Treveal* continued to float offshore for several days, before sinking a kilometre offshore. She was returning from Calcutta, on her maiden voyage with a cargo of manganese, which remains largely intact at 8 fathoms.

Limestone crags: overlooking Chapman's Pool and St Alban's Head.

 97 ST ALBAN'S HEAD

The southern-most tip of the Isle of Purbeck, St Alban's Head (SY 961 754) is always known as such locally and by mariners, but its Norman chapel with a single window is dedicated to St Aldhelm. He was the first Bishop of Sherborne. St Alban, the first British martyr, was killed about 304 in the Roman town that now bears his name. It is quite possible that both names have been attached to the headland for a millennium, with St Alban being the Celtic original and St Aldhelm the Saxon successor, as the chapel stands inside what is probably an earlier encircling earthwork.

Norman chapel: just inland from the Coastguard look-out on St Alban's Head.

The chapel, an exact square of just under 10 metres, is said to have been built as a chantry, in about 1175, for the performance of masses in aid of those passing by at sea. It built entirely of stone near the edge of the cliff on a limestone plateau at 353 feet above sea-level. Clearly visible from out at sea, the altitude at the top of its stone cross – on the apex of a pyramid-shaped roof – was stated by John Austen in 1857 to be 379 feet. He considered the traces of a metre diameter 'cylindrical foundation' below the cross and the supporting square pillar below 'to have been originally designed to support some weighty superstructure' which 'might have been a beacon, or some species of lighthouse'.

Thomas Bond told Austen that it was known as the Devil's Chapel 'amongst the rural population of the neighbourhood' and that before repair by Lord Eldon the stone roof was ruined and overgrown with grass. Villagers from Worth Matravers, 1½ kilometres inland, made an annual pilgrimage to the headland on Whit Thursday. They would 'proceed with music'. Having dressed the chapel with flags they danced inside it. Pins were inserted into a hole in the central pillar by young women wishing for a husband.

'St Alban's Head' is the name that appears on its Coastguard lookout which is now manned by the volunteers of National Coastwatch. Below, on a wide quarry shelf, are the concrete footings of a wartime radar station. On the edge stands a mushroomed-shape rock, from the original cliff-face, left by quarrymen as a seamark.

Below – *Sculpted seamark: the quarrymen left this chunk of St Alban's Head.* Below right – *National Coastwatch: archetypal setting for the maritime lookout on St Alban's Head.*

98 WINSPIT and KEATES QUARRY

The cliffside galleries at the seaward end of Winspit Bottom (SY 976 761), south of Worth Matravers, were worked from 1700 to 1945. The underground opening south-east of Winspit Cottage is now sealed with an iron grill which lets in horseshoe and other rare species of bats, both to breed and for hibernation, while protecting them from human interference. Seawards, on either side of a rocky cleft, the cliffside has been worked from ledges, with the quarry buildings being on the western side.

The local names for the beds were listed in 1895 and corrected for me by the last quarryman, William Jeremiah Bower (1886-1966), who was always known as Billy Winspit. He described them as Burr, Shrimpstone, Bluestone, Pond Freestone, Flintstone, Listy Bed, House Cap, Underpicking Cap, Under Freestone and Cliff Beds (chert).

These galleries appear to be those described by John Smeaton when he surveyed West Country quarries before building the Eddystone Lighthouse in 1757. He said it was harder than Portland stone and more difficult to work, with a 'somewhat precarious' method of shipment in which it was lowered by ropes into waiting boats and taken along the coast to Swanage, which 'can only be done in very moderate weathers'.

Winspit Bottom: the valley between Worth Matravers and the sea.

Winspit Cottage: the home of last quarryman Billy Winspit.

Sea thrift: flourishing on the cliffs of southern Purbeck.

Western seaboard: the stone cliffs from Winspit to St Alban's Head.

I found Billy Winspit chipping away at a fireplace. It turned out to be a fortnight before he died, when he told me that 16 cubic feet of the cliffs represented a ton of stone. He also told me about set-netting the mackerel shoals, and how the two jobs went together:

'My father before me worked the quarries like I do, and granfer worked on the cliffs, and his father. When I was a boy, father and I worked underground. In the old fashioned way you moved the stone out, cut it, and sent it to London in blocks. But all that is finished with now and I only do a carving job as a part-time. Once I had a 14-foot boat and went fishing in the summer as well. You couldn't do it in winter as we have some terrific weather here – seas 50 feet high. I have seen the waves come over the cliff into the quarry.'

He stopped to sharpen some tools as he had done since the age of sixteen, when he became the quarry's blacksmith. He had started quarrying at the age of eleven, in Queen Victoria's Diamond Jubilee year of 1897, and recalled that a decade later pay was £1-5s-0d. a week and £11 was the total weekly wage bill for Winspit Quarries. Until his death, oil lamps gave the only light in stone-roofed Winspit Cottage, which had neither gas or electricity.

He told me about playing his fiddle in the Square and Compass, named for the Masonic tools of the trade, on the hillside in Worth village. That was during the reign of publican Charlie Newman, who died at 82, in coronation year, 1953. Their best remembered guest was the wild-living artist Augustus John from Fryern Court, near Fordingbridge.

Inland, the National Trust bought the strip lynchets along the valley slopes of East Man, to the road into Worth Matravers, in 1999. These, and the even larger collection facing them on West Man, are among the best preserved mediaeval cultivation terraces in the British Isles.

The National Trust also owns Keates Quarry, east of the village, where it preserves a splendid array of more than 100 sauropod prints, up to 111 cm in diameter. Purbeck provides the only British examples of multiple dinosaur footprints. Most, including those at Worth, come from the Middle Purbeck layer which spans the Late Jurassic and Early Cretaceous boundary of 145 million years ago.

Kevin Keates discovered the best ever British find of fossil footprints in 1997 when he drove a digger and was in the process of removing unwanted freestone from the top of a level of the Middle Purbeck beds which he was intending to cut and lift. This was the Bottom Freestone (as known to quarrymen) or the Intermarine Member of the

Lulworth Formation (as described by geologists). The remarkable set of prints, running for 200 metres, were studied by Dr Jo Wright before being carefully covered to prevent erosion:

'It is the biggest dinosaur tracksite found in Britain, and as such is of international importance. The site was excavated and investigated with the support of the National Trust. The footprints were made by sauropod dinosaurs and the present track surface is the actual layer on which the animals walked. The tracks were made by more than one individual - probably more than 12. At the time of track formation this site was a shelly beach beside a freshwater lagoon. The tracksite is the only evidence for the presence of sauropod dinosaurs in the Purbeck Limestone Group because no skeletal remains of these dinosaurs have been found in these sediments. The discovery of the site means that all the major groups of dinosaurs around in the Cretaceous are now known in Purbeck from footprints.'

Pot fishing: off Seacombe in high summer.

99 SEACOMBE

Biggest and best of the Purbeck cliffside workings, Seacombe Quarry (SY 984 766) has cavernous openings, worked to an average height of 3 metres and extending deep into the hillside. It lies on the south-west side of Seacombe Bottom, reached from the cliff path or down a farm track from the Priest's Way at Eastington. Great pieces of work

Eastern cliffs: from Seacombe to Dancing Ledge and Anvil Point.

Old quarries: the Seacombe workings are now reserved for the bats.

were carved and taken out from here, with added value to justify road transport, rather than the cheaper sea trip to Swanage. In 1871, A. Bower's quarry was commissioned to cut a 3.5 ton trough for North Woolwich Galvanising Works. Its dimensions were 8 feet long, 4 feet wide, and 4 feet deep.

Both the Basebed and the Whitbed – the latter over 2 metres thick – were worked. The stone is Portland, rather than Purbeck, from the uppermost stratum of the Jurassic system. Portland stone is marine in origin whereas Purbeck is a freshwater limestone. The Portland-Purbeck stone at Seacombe was taken out in blocks of 15 tons and the roofs of the underground galleries are between 3 and 4 metres high. Huge pillars support them but there are rock-falls, inevitably, as they were never intended to stand for centuries. It is unsafe to wander into them, and fencing also prevents the cattle going into them for summer shade, all access having been sealed. Even a hard-hat would give only cosmetic protection.

These great quarries were in use from 1700 to 1930. Trucks returned in the Second World War for spoil as the hard-core for military aerodromes across the heathlands of the New Forest.

Westwards, below the Halsewell Stile in a blackthorn hedge, the Halsewell Rock (SY 981 764) preserves the memory of a dramatic shipwreck. It took place at 02.00 hours on Friday 6 January 1786 and provided Charles Dickens with the material for *The Long Voyage*. In fact the final journey of the *Halsewell*, a 758-ton East Indiaman, was tragically short as she was outward bound from Gravesend to Bengal. Having lost masts and rigging in a gale, she failed to turn into the Solent, and Captain Richard Pierce found himself driven into the vertical cliffs of southern Purbeck in a blizzard.

The oldest captain of the East India Company, Richard Pierce was accompanied by two daughters and two nieces, and was intending to retire on return to India. They were among the 168 who were drowned. Only 82 seamen survived, through clawing their way out of the waves and clinging to the Halsewell Rock from where they were rescued by ropes lowered down the 100-feet cliff by quarrymen 'at the imminent hazard of their own lives'.

The dead were buried beneath low mounds in Seacombe Bottom and the graves marked by guns recovered from the wreck. These had disappeared within fifty years. Other items were salvaged from the ship, including a mirror in the parish church at Worth Matravers, a green hour-glass now in Dorset County Museum at Dorchester, and cupboards at Corfe Castle and Swanage. The pintle, a bronze hinge which held the rudder, was recovered by divers in 1973.

Digging had taken place in 1972, without success, to find the graves. There is unlikely to be further disturbance on the ground as the land from the Halsewell Stile, eastwards across Seacombe Bottom, came into National Trust ownership after Kingston Lacy landowner Ralph Bankes died in 1981.

Wartime relic: for a machine-gunner, overlooking the cliffs from Seacombe to Winspit.

100 HEDBURY and TOPMAST QUARRY

The last puffins and auks such as guillemots and razorbills, once a commonplace along this coast, can be seen along the stone cliffs in the vicinity of Hedbury Quarry (SY 993 767) and Topmast Quarry (SY 995 768). Though not given its name by the Ordnance Survey, Hedbury derives from the Eidbury family, rather than the 'Headbury' spelling given in the Langton Matravers tithe map of 1838. The Eidburys opened the quarry in the mid-eighteenth century and expanded into the fourth-largest along this coast. Ironwork and a holed stone set above the waves show the site of its whim derrick used to lower stone into boats. No road led out of Hedbury.

There is also a 12-pounder cannon, probably from a shipwreck, which lay among abandoned blocks of cut stone until being mounted on a plinth and set pointing seawards. Topmast Quarry, a miniature version of Hedbury is 200 metres to the east.

Shipwrecked cannon: Channel view from Hedbury to St Alban's Head.

Hedbury came into National Trust ownership with the Corfe Castle Estate, bequeathed by Ralph Bankes in 1982, and Topmast Quarry joined it with the acquisition of the coast around Dancing Ledge in 1993.

Dancing Ledge: with sea and surf doing just that.

101 DANCING LEDGE and BLACKER'S HOLE

The romantic name Dancing Ledge (SY 998 769) aptly describes the ribbon of waves that often splash across a shelf left by eighteenth- and nineteenth-century quarrymen. The Hayward family were the original operators. Its tripod-shaped whim – the derrick or crane used to lower cut blocks into boats which carried the stone to Swanage – stood on the cliff-edge until about 1930 when it was taken to St Aldhelm's Quarry, inland from St Alban's Head.

Their quarrymen cut a swimming pool, into the Dancing Ledge, in the 1890s, so that the boys of Durnford School, 1½ kilometres inland at Langton Matravers, were no longer excused their morning swim when the sea was too rough. Headmaster Thomas Pellatt, the father of Tudor biographer Hester Chapman (1899-1976), instigated a morning exercise ritual in which the boys ran to Dancing Ledge and then stripped. They lined up naked, waiting for Pellatt to arrive, and then jumped one by one from a diving board into the sea.

Swimming pool: cut by the quarrymen for Durnford schoolboys.

Such practices, before his time, would have inspired avant garde film director Derek Jarman (1942-97) who made home-movies here with friends and lovers, also generally without their clothes. A volume of his autobiography is entitled *Dancing Ledge*.

To the east, the cliffs above Blacker's Hole (SZ 007 769) are noted for their colonies of the rare early spider orchid. A double set of steel masts, and a matching pair a nautical mile eastwards at Anvil Point, were erected for warships undertaking speed trials.

Dancing Ledge came into National Trust ownership in 1993, with 190 acres of Spyway Farm inland to the Priest's Way and Langton Matravers, through Enterprise Neptune funds and a bequest from S. E. N. Whitelock. Another 117 acres were added to the east, above Blacker's Hole, in 1994 and 155 acres to the north-east, at Putlake Farm, in 1996.

Spyway Farm: National Trust pastures from the sea to Langton.

102 BELLE VUE CLIFFS and RAGGED ROCKS

Immediately west of Durlston Country Park, the three fields of Belle Vue Cliffs (SZ 015 770) extend for 700 metres above 150-feet Purbeck stone cliffs. Eastwards are the Ragged Rocks (SZ 021 768), in an offshore ribbon which breaks the waves to Anvil Point, and immediately down below is the cliffside known as Half Moon (SZ 017 768).

The fields cover 51 acres and are owned by the National Trust, having been bought in 1976 with a donation from L. Forder in memory of his wife, Mrs E. A. E. Forder.

103 ROUND DOWN and ANVIL POINT

Midway between those on Portland Bill and The Needles, the Lighthouse on Anvil Point (SZ 029 769) was completed in 1881. It failed to save the 1250-ton sailing ship *Alexandrovna* of Liverpool which was smashed against rocks below the 80-feet cliffs by a hurricane on 29 April 1882. None of the 77 crew survived. The following Thursday the Bournemouth paddle-steamer *Empress* brought a large party of visitors to view the wreck with 'much excitement' being generated as a naked body was found in a lifebuoy. Many others were being washed up 'bruised and disfigured'. Reports appeared in newspapers across middle England of 'clouds of salt-spray' being blown 160 kilometres inland. Coastal trees had been completely stripped of their young leaves and the elms at Swanage were not back in leaf until after midsummer.

On the rising ground of Round Down (SY 025 771), 500 metres north-west of the Lighthouse, a Royal Navy Signal Station was in operation during the Napoleonic

Wars. It initially relayed shore to ship orders by telegraph, on the system devised by Sir Home Riggs Popham (1762-1820) and then by semaphore using a great upright hoarding of circles and squares in the style of an oversized cricket scoreboard. Stony foundations of a walled enclosure, with six military buildings, can still be traced. They are grouped around a depression, 5½ metres by 6 metres, that marks the site of the signals apparatus.

Both Anvil Point and Round Down are now part of Durlston Country Park.

Squat tower: the Lighthouse on Anvil Point lacks stature but has a prominent position.

Durlston Castle: built as a seaside villa, on top of the headland.

104 DURLSTON CASTLE and THE GREAT GLOBE

An eccentric mason and contractor brought discarded London monuments to Swanage and devised his own fairy-tale seascape with the building of Durlston Castle (SZ 035 772) and installation of a 40-ton Great Globe. George Burt (1816-94) was described by Thomas Hardy as 'the King of Swanage'. What is now a corbelled-turreted restaurant was built in 1887 as a palatial French Riviera-style villa in Purbeck stone on land which Burt bought in 1864. Three granule pillars were ordered by Sir Charles Barry for Trafalgar Square but were purloined by Burt on being rejected as surplus to requirements. 'Durlston Head Castle, above sea 215 feet,' its inscription tells us.

Such carvings are everywhere. They quote cosmic facts, rock-related scripture, and the great poets. The visiting rules are also cut in stone. We are told not to shoot or throw stones and to restrict writing our names 'to this stone only'.

Scientific information abounds around the Great Globe which was carved in Portland stone at the late John Mowlem's Greenwich works in 1887. It was brought to Swanage in 15 segments and raised on a platform 'Above sea 136 ft'. Just over 3 metres in diameter, it portrays continents, oceans and rivers rather than geopolitical boundaries.

Some of the smallest but most interesting of Purbeck fossils have come from above Durlston Bay, beside the scenic path that George Burt called Isle of Wight Road (SZ 034 773), only metres from its junction with the Round the Head path. Small shrew-like mammals, marsupials dating from 65 million years ago, are the prototypes of all advanced creatures, ourselves included. The ubiquitous dinosaurs disappear at this point from the fossil record. Worldwide evidence is that the Earth suffered a cosmic catastrophe, perhaps having been hit by an asteroid, which was probably smaller than the Isle of Purbeck.

Below left – *Durlston Restaurant: Riviera-style flourishes at Durlston Head Castle.* Below – *The Globe: ten feet in diameter, made at Greenwich in 1887, seen from above the Pacific.*

105 DURLSTON COUNTRY PARK and TILLY WHIM CAVES

An imaginative and foresighted creation, Durlston Country Park was instigated by Dorset County Council in 1974 on coastal downland on and around Durlston Head, at the south end of Lighthouse Road, Swanage (SZ 033 772). Chief executive Kenneth Abel and county planning officer Alan Swindall briefed me on a management plan that sought to preserve 'the rich ecological pattern' through a 'careful balance between people and nature'. Seabirds on the cliffs and orchids across Round Down had survived the intensive use of the area as a Victorian and Edwardian playground. Modern difficulties included subterranean access problems in Tilly Whim Caves (SZ 031 769) where the collapsing roof of an early nineteenth-century underground quarry resulted in its being closed to the public. Burgeoning health and safety legislation has kept it sealed-off.

Below – *Lone figures: above and below the remains of Tilly Whim Caves.* Below right – *Durlston Bay: from Isle of Wight Road to Peveril Point.*

Long running friction between ornithologists and climbers was easier to resolve. Talks resulted in a workable truce in no-go sanctuaries and seasonal closed areas are offset by unrestricted access elsewhere. These climbs rank among the most popular in Britain. Classic ones have their own names, such as Rendezvous Manque, between Durlston Head and Tilly Whim Caves, and Traverse of the Gods between Tilly Whim and Anvil Point. On the latter is the Subliminal Cliff which claimed an ordinary walker who stumbled over it in 1999. Westwards are Via Christina, Nutcracker Exit, Marmolata Buttress, Sheerline, Bottomless Buttress and Boulder Ruckle Exit.

Offshore, coinciding with their increasing losses from entanglement in fishing nets in the Bay of Biscay, the return of schools of porpoises and bottle-nosed dolphins is monitored from Durlston Head. Binocular-carrying 'Dolphin Watch' volunteers carry out the equivalent of a marine traffic census.

106 PEVERIL POINT and the CLOCK TOWER

The Purbeck marble ledges of Peveril Point (SZ 040 786), guarded by fortifications from Elizabethan times until the Second World War, are still overlooked by a National Coastwatch lookout which was rebuilt in 2000. Westwards, towards Swanage, are former Coastguard Cottages, and the Lifeboat Station which has been operational since 1875.

Peveril ledges: eastern extremity of the Purbeck marble beds.

Southern shore: Clock Tower and boatyard with stumps of an earlier pier.

Beside it are slipways and a boatyard, at Rockleigh, which is overshadowed by a clock-less Gothic Clock Tower (SZ 037 786). Designed as a memorial to the Duke of Wellington (1769-1852) it was erected at the Southwark end of London Bridge, in 1854, to hold the transparent dials of a clock made for the Great Exhibition of 1851. Traffic vibration made it a poor time-keeper and the Metropolitan Police called it 'an unwarrantable obstruction'. Demolition took place in 1866 after the building of a railway viaduct put it out of sight.

Retired London contractor Thomas Docwra, who had just bought The Grove as his 'marine residence', brought the Clock Tower to Swanage for re-building as the north-eastern corner of his new property. The Grove was later turned into the Hotel Grosvenor, by the Exton family, and greatly expanded between 1902 and 1927. A secret royal visit, by King George VI, took place on the night of 17 April 1944. He was awoken at 04.00 in the morning and taken to Fort Henry on Redend Point, Studland, to watch large-scale rehearsals of the forthcoming D-Day landings. Aerial bombardment and live ammunition made Exercise Smash the most realistic of a series of practice assault landings.

The Hotel Grosvenor was demolished in 1986 and replaced by continental-style villas. Two classical columns, which formed the centrepiece of its facade, were re-erected on the adjoining Peveril Downs open space (SZ 035 785).

Swanage Pier: an English Victorian institution, restored for the new millennium.

107 SWANAGE BAY

Seaside Swanage replaced a bustling quarry port by stages through the nineteenth century, starting with the opening by William Morton Pitt of the Manor House Hotel (SZ 033 787) in 1827. Looking out across Swanage Bay, it became the Victoria Hotel after the visit of Princess Victoria in August 1833, and the Royal Victoria Hotel on being sold after Pitt's death, by which time Victoria was Queen. Conversion to flats took place in 1978.

The evolution of the leisure resort gathered pace with the building of the first Swanage Pier (SZ 037 787), by James Walton of London, in 1859. It was supplemented, and then replaced, by the present pier constructed by Alfred Thorne of Westminster, in 1895. Both attracted paddle-steamers, from Bournemouth and Weymouth, with the tradition now being maintained by the annual return of the PS *Waverley*.

Stone was still being brought to yards beside the shore, called bankers, until the turn of the twentieth century when the Edwardian shops of Institute Road and the apartments of The Parade arose from its debris (SZ 032 788). Northwards, the Mowlem

Swanage Bay: looking towards the eastern end of the World Heritage Site at Old Harry Rocks.

Institute provided by Swanage-born contractor John Mowlem (1788-1868) survived until 1966, when it was replaced by the present Mowlem theatre and restaurant.

Beside it, incongruously topped by four Russian cannon balls from the Crimean War, Mowlem's Column commemorates a battle which never took place, long before the invention of gunpowder. It was not a naval engagement but Purbeck's earliest recorded shipwrecks that changed the course of English history. In 876, after months of fighting, the West Saxons bribed the Danes, who had sailed into Wareham to negotiate a truce. They promised King Alfred they would leave Wessex but instead of going home they went to Exeter.

The shipwrecks took place in 877. Three versions of the *Anglo-Saxon Chronicle* say a Danish fleet 'encountered a great storm at sea, and 120 ships were lost at Swanage'. Another two manuscripts refer to 'a great mist at sea' as the cause of the fortuitous disaster. It could well have been a combination of foul weather. Disorientation in thick fog, followed by an easterly gale – the direction to which Swanage is exposed – resulted in the failure of the full Danish force to reach Exeter. The remainder acceded to Alfred's demands and quit the city, leaving for Gloucester, which lay in Mercian territory.

108 BALLARD DOWN and PUNFIELD COVE

The eastern extremity of the Purbeck Hills, forming the backdrop to Swanage streets and its seaside, Ballard Down rises to 526 feet (SZ 027 812) in a long hog's back ridge from the Ulwell Gap to Ballard Point. The northern slope of Ballard Down has a superb chalkland flora, packed with orchids and bellflowers though the much drier and exposed southern side has far less species.

Below the west end of Ballard Cliff is Punfield Cove (SZ 040 810), now an eroded undercliff, which held a swan-pool until 1705. Then Swanage quarrymen broke up its retaining wall for boulders to complete a consignment of stone for repairing dykes in the Netherlands. South-westwards, a section of Wealden sands includes the highly fossiliferous Punfield marine band, with Spanish affinities. This lies in the Cretaceous layers of the final Mesozoic period when colourful lower greensand was accumulating in warm coastal waters.

Ballard Point, known in Swanage as Ballard Head, forms the distinctive northern profile of Swanage Bay. Studland farmers, Julian Homer of the National Trust tells me, knew it as East Hill around the 383-feet triagulation pillar. The next field to the west, where the Trust has now taken land out of arable farming and restored chalk grassland, was called Bomb Hill. He heard of a Second World War bomb blast but there is a much longer history of military training here, dating back to mid-Victorian times, when Dorset Rifle Volunteers frequently held their main summer camp at Whitecliff Farm.

Ballard Down: with the Waverley *passing the fresh white gash of a landslip, in 2001.*

The southern slopes of Ballard Down, south-westwards from the disused rifle range to valley suburbia at Whitecliff Farm, Swanage, were bought by the National Trust through its Enterprise Neptune appeal in 1976.

109 OLD HARRY ROCKS and PARSON'S BARN

The chalk sea-stacks of Old Harry Rocks, Turf Rick Rock and The Pinnacles (SZ 055 825) are Dorset's cretaceous equivalent of Devon's older sandstone pillars in Ladram Bay. Old Harry was accompanied by Old Harry's Wife until she collapsed in the 1896 storm that washed away the old chain-pier at Brighton.

Otherwise known as Handfast Point, this was the site of Studland Castle, re-fortified as one of Henry VIII's chain of South Coast block-houses. It jutted north-eastwards from the present Old Harry Rocks and was positioned to guard the Swash Channel approach into Poole Harbour. There was also a mediaeval predecessor, as Thomas Gerard makes clear, writing in about 1624. He says 'the land stretcheth forth a short promontory furnished with a block-house, for the more grace called Studland Castle, upon which it abutteth'. All traces of both buildings have been taken by the sea.

Below the main cliff, named ironically because in the time of tithes there was none bigger, is a large sea-level cavern known as Parson's Barn (SZ 053 822). Legends attach to the headland of the mediaeval Poole pirate Harry Paye and to the other Harry, the Devil himself, with the clifftop pasture being Old Nick's Ground. The gap between it and Old Harry is known as St Lucas Leap from the memory of a greyhound that made the jump after a rabbit disappeared over the edge. Birds breeding in its unreachable recesses include cormorants and sand martins with ledges also being home to peregrine falcons and ravens.

The Devon and Dorset World Heritage Site ends as it began, at Old Harry as on Orcombe Point, with an expanse of National Trust land which includes almost all of the view over the parish of Studland. It came to the Trust after the death of its greatest benefactor, Ralph Bankes, a year to the day after his death on 19 August 1981. He bequeathed to the nation Kingston Lacy House and its art collection, and the ruins of Corfe Castle, plus 16,000 acres of superlative scenery including the best sandy beaches in England.

The opulent shore from Sandbanks and Canford Cliffs to Bournemouth and Hengistbury Head forms the northern backdrop to the view from Old Harry. Eastwards, linked by the sea that divides them, the chalk formations from Purbeck resume at The Needles on the Isle of Wight. Up to 10,000 years ago you could have walked across the bay. That opportunity awaits in the next Ice Age, locking so much water into glaciers that sea levels will drop by 100 feet, which puts our coast into the context of geological time.

Handfast Point: Old Harry Rocks and the Bournemouth skyline.